Mathematical
for E

Mathematical Modelling for Economists

Donald A.R. George

MACMILLAN
EDUCATION

First published 1988

Published by
MACMILLAN EDUCATION LTD
Houndmills, Basingstoke, Hampshire RG21 2XS
and London
Companies and representatives
throughout the world

Distributed in the USA
by Basil Blackwell, New York

Printed in Hong Kong

British Library Cataloguing in Publication Data
George, Donald A.R.
Mathematical modelling for economists.
1. Economics — Mathematical models
I. Title
511'.8'02433   HB135
ISBN 0–333–42443–3 (hardcover)
ISBN 0–333–42444–1 (paperback)

To my mother and father

Contents

Preface

Model building is an activity which students often find difficult and sometimes rather puzzling. It can be difficult to see just how the latest 97-equation model with 35 parameters and 53 variables can have any relevance to the great problems of economics such as unemployment, poverty, distribution and growth. Students are frequently tempted to skip the 'nasty mathematical bit' in journal articles, and yet model building is an indispensable aspect of modern economics.

The mathematics explained in this book is really quite easy but the process of model building requires skills other than simply knowing the appropriate mathematics. It is a process of abstraction involving the construction, manipulation and interpretation of models and this book places considerable emphasis on these issues. Modelling is thus treated as a fairly 'down-to-earth' procedure. We eschew the grand questions of the modern scholastics and the reader wishing to know how many equilibria can dance on a compact manifold will therefore have to look elsewhere. Having read the book, students should be able to understand the majority of models used in the general economics journals and even to construct and use simple models of their own.

This book is based on courses given at Edinburgh and I am grateful to generations of Edinburgh students who never fail to offer comments and criticisms on the material with which they are presented. The book was revised while I was on leave at the European University Institute, Florence, to whom I am indebted for a generous Fellowship and an opportunity to work surrounded by Tuscan hills and endless supplies of Chianti. I am grateful also for the constructive and stimulating discussions I have had with colleagues both in Edinburgh and in Florence. I would mention in particular Simon Clark (Edinburgh) who read the entire manuscript and provided much useful advice. I am also particularly grateful to Les Oxley (Edinburgh), who has permitted me to draw upon research we have conducted jointly, and to Robert Kast

(Florence). Any remaining errors or omissions are, of course, my own. Chris Barton and Jessica Spataro, who can interpret Icelandic Runestones with ease, dealt swiftly with my dreadful handwriting, turning it efficiently into typescript; for this I am most grateful. Thanks also to Jennifer Pegg and Keith Povey for guiding the book through the editorial and production processes. Finally, my greatest debt is to my parents, for their unfailing support and encouragement in all my endeavours, including those even less reputable than textbook writing.

Florence   DONALD A.R. GEORGE

1 Models, theories and method

Consider an Economics student presented with the following mathematical relationships:

$$x = \alpha z + \beta \quad\quad\quad (1.1)$$
$$q = \bar{q} \quad\quad\quad (1.2)$$
$$z = x + y \quad\quad\quad (1.3)$$
$$w = x + q \quad\quad\quad (1.4)$$
$$w = z \quad\quad\quad (1.5)$$

and suppose he or she is told that equations (1.1)–(1.5) imply:

$$\frac{\mathrm{d}z}{\mathrm{d}\bar{q}} = \frac{1}{1-\alpha} \quad (\alpha \neq 1) \quad\quad\quad (1.6)$$

He or she is probably not going to be particularly enlightened by this information. Suppose now that the variables in equations (1.1)–(1.5) are simply relabelled thus:

$$C = aY + b \quad\quad\quad (1.1')$$
$$I = \bar{I} \qu\quad\quad\quad (1.2')$$
$$Y = C + S \quad\quad\quad (1.3')$$
$$E = C + I \quad\quad\quad (1.4')$$
$$E = Y \quad\quad\quad (1.5')$$

The familiar Keynesian-cross model of aggregate income determination is now self-evident and equation (1.6) yields the well-known result relating the investment multiplier $\mathrm{d}Y/\mathrm{d}\bar{I}$ to the marginal propensity to consume (a):

$$\frac{\mathrm{d}Y}{\mathrm{d}\bar{I}} = \frac{1}{1-a} \quad\quad\quad (1.6')$$

Equations (1.1)–(1.6) constitute a simple *mathematical model* of aggregate income determination. The model consists of a number of mathematical relationships (equations (1.1)–(1.5)) together with a conclusion (equation (1.6)) deduced from them in a mathematically correct way. Equations $(1.1')$–$(1.6')$ simply duplicate this model but, by using more suggestive variable names, make it easier to understand. A mathematical model then is a set of mathematical relationships, called *assumptions*, together with some conclusions, correctly deduced from them. It is a purely *logical* construct with no empirical meaning. This is illustrated above by expressing the familiar Keynesian-cross model in unfamiliar notations. To acquire an empirical meaning a model requires *interpretation*. For example the variable x in equation (1.1) can be relabelled 'C' in equation $(1.1')$ and interpreted as 'aggregate consumption', as measured by some statistic in the 'Blue Book'. Equation (1.3) or $(1.3')$ can be interpreted as an accounting *identity*:

$$Y \equiv C + S \qquad (1.3'')$$

where Y = national income
  S = savings

An identity is an equation (sometimes written with the symbol $\equiv$ in place of the usual equals symbol $=$) which is true *by definition of its variables*. Thus equation $(1.3')$ is an identity because savings are *defined* to mean income which is not consumed.

Interpretation is not confined to the assumption of a model, it extends also to the conclusions. Economics students will be familiar with various difficulties associated with the interpretation of equation (1.6) or $(1.6')$. It certainly does *not* mean that an increase of £1 bn in GDCF today will lead to an increase of $1/(1-\alpha) \times$ £1 bn in GNP tomorrow.

A model then can be thought of as the logical, 'hardcore' of a theory. Its assumptions are derived through a process of *abstraction*. That is, the 'real world' problem to be analysed is simplified and its key features expressed mathematically. The assumptions of a model, and in particular what constitutes a 'key feature' of the real world, will clearly depend on the theoretical position of the modeller. To criticise a model for omitting some aspect of the 'real world' is always a vacuous procedure since *all* models involve abstraction and hence omission of some aspect of the real world problem. What is and is not included in a model will depend on the theoretical standpoint of the modeller and on the purpose for which the model is being built. This latter point can be illustrated by considering the non-mathematical models constructed in another discipline: aero-engineering. It is standard practice to construct physical models of new aircraft and place them in wind tunnels to test their aerodynamic properties. These tests are in no way jeopardised by the omission from the model of the colour of the air-hostess' uniform.

The assumptions of a model then, are derived from a process of abstraction which is certainly selective and which reflects the theoretical standpoint of the modeller. Having stated the model's assumptions, an immediate test of its validity can be applied. The assumptions must be *mutually consistent*, that is it must be possible for all to be true simultaneously. Consistency is essential since, from inconsistent assumptions one can derive *any* proposition: that the Moon is made of cheese, that kangaroos play tennis, for example.

Secondly one may insist that at least some of the variables in the model can be interpreted as *empirically measurable* magnitudes. This need not be true of all variables. In a utility maximising model of consumer behaviour for example, it is hard to see how utility itself can be measured though the elasticity of (market) demand may well be. It is often the case that the measurability requirement is imposed on the variables of a model's conclusions though not necessarily on those of its assumptions. This is because many economists seek to *test* a model's *conclusions* but not necessarily its assumptions. This point is returned to later.

Thirdly, one must require that the model's conclusions be deduced from its assumptions in a mathematically correct way.

The art of model building then consists of abstraction, deduction, and interpretation. The greater part of this book is concerned with deduction; the mathematically correct derivation of conclusions from assumptions. It is here that the careful application of mathematics is essential. The other aspects of modelling are not omitted however, and in practice are just as important as the deduction of conclusions from assumptions.

The process of modelling has the merit of forcing precision on the economist. He or she is obliged to make a precise statement of assumptions and to show precisely how his or her conclusions follow from them. Wicksteed (1894) certainly saw mathematical argument as offering advantages over less precise methods:

The mathematical form of statement (acts) as a safeguard against unconscious assumptions, and as a reagent that will *precipitate* the assumptions held in solution in the verbiage of our ordinary disquisitions,

However, there will typically be an infinite number of models consistent with any given theory and the choice as to which model to develop must be a matter of judgement.

One may legitimately ask whether mathematical modelling contributes to progress in Economics; whether it has any real purpose. The mathematical approach has certainly contributed substantially in natural sciences like Physics but one may perhaps be less certain about social sciences such as Economics. It has been suggested that difficult mathematical analysis provides an effective 'barrier to entry' to the discipline of economics, enabling economists to disguise relatively simple ideas in a cloak of impenetrable formalism. Many students, asked to plough through three articles from *Econometrica* by next Tuesday, have come to agree with this view. In his 'Life among the Econ' Axel Leijonhufvud (1981) likens Economists to a tribe (the 'Econ') of which the 'Math-Econ' form the 'priestly caste'. The importance of models to the Econ is substantial, according to Leijonhufvud:

> The facts (a) that the Econ are highly status motivated, (b) that status is only to be achieved by making "modls" and (c) that most of these "modls" seem to be of little or no practical use, probably accounts for the backwardness and abject cultural poverty of the tribe . . .
> . . . The rise of the Math-Econ seems to be associated with the previously noted trend among all the Econ towards more ornate, ceremonial modls. . . .

To some economists it has seemed that Economics must adopt mathematical methods simply because it deals with *quantitative* issues. This view seems to be independent of any notion of modelling. Jevons (1965), for example, is quite clear on the importance of mathematics:

> It is clear that Economics, if it is to be a science at all, must be a mathematical science. There exists much prejudice against attempts to introduce the methods and language of mathematics into any branch of the moral sciences. Many persons seem to

think that the physical sciences form the sphere of mathematical method and that the moral sciences demand some other method – I know not what. My theory of Economics, however, is purely mathematical in character. Nay, believing that the quantities with which we deal must be subject to continuous variation, I do not hesitate to use the appropriate branch of mathematical science, involving though it does the fearless consideration of infinitely small quantities. The theory consists in applying the differential calculus to the familiar notions of wealth, utility, value, demand, supply, capital, interest, labour and all the other quantitative notions belonging to the daily operation of industry. As the complete theory of almost every other science involves the use of that calculus, so we cannot have a true theory of economics without its aid.

To me it seems that *our science must be mathematical simply because it deals with quantities*.

To some economists it has seemed that the adoption of a mathematical modelling approach imparts an ideological or political bias to Economics, since mathematical methods seem better adapted to some theoretical perspectives than to others. The application of calculus to develop the ideas of the Marginalists is perhaps an example. Some Western Marxists have suggested that the mathematical approach is inappropriate for the development of Marxist ideas, despite attempts by Morishima (1973) and Steedman (1977), among others, to 'mathematise Marx'. The Soviet Nobel-laureate L.V. Kantorovich (1959), however, takes the following view:

Equally unjustified is the prejudice against mathematical methods because of their partial use by bourgeois economic schools. Clearly, the precedents of the incorrect use of mathematics for purposes different from ours cannot prevent Soviet scientists from using mathematical methods in economic problems in a way which is correct and of advantage in the building of communism.

It would be foolish to deny that *individual economists* are politically and ideologically biased, but it is hard to see how mathematical modelling *per se* imparts any such bias. One must, however, treat the economic problems and not the mathematical methods as primary, and develop models accordingly. Economic ideas should not be rejected or ignored simply because they seem difficult to capture with standard modelling techniques. It may be necessary to develop new techniques, perhaps utilising novel branches of mathematics.

Thus far a distinction has been maintained between *models* and *theories*. Some economists posit a very close relationship between the two. Accepting the role of models in making precise the relationship between assumptions and conclusions, Koopmans (1957) goes on to argue that we should:

> look upon Economic theory as a sequence of conceptional [*sic*] *models* that seek to express in simplified form different aspects of an always more complicated reality. At first these aspects are formalised as much as feasible in isolation, then in combinations of increasing realism. Each model is defined by a set of postulates, of which the implications are developed to the extent deemed worthwhile in relation to the aspects of reality expressed by the postulates. The study of the simpler models is protected from the reproach of unreality by the consideration that these models may be prototypes of more realistic but also more complicated, subsequent models. The card file of successfully completed pieces of reasoning represented by these models can then be looked upon as the logical core of economics, as the depository of available economic theory.

It is probably useful to maintain a sharper distinction between models and theories. A model, as has been said, is a purely logical construction, while a theory consists of a coherent set of hypotheses with empirical (or 'synthetic') content, designed to provide explanations of observable phenomena. It is sometimes argued that the importance of models lies in their role in the *testing* of theories. Models can be constructed in such a way as to embody certain of a theory's hypotheses and to apply them to some particular problem. It may well be the case that the conclusions of a model are easier to test than its assumptions. Thus models provide a crucial link in the application and testing of theories. There is of course, considerable argument as to whether one should test the hypotheses of a theory or its predictions. This controversy lies beyond the scope of this book, but the interested reader will find it dealt with in the references mentioned in the 'further reading' section at the end of the chapter.

In any event, one can see a role for models in theory appraisal on the grounds discussed implicitly in the above quotation from Jevons, that most testing procedures are quantitative. Thus one function of models in modern economics is to provide a link between the hypotheses of theory and the data of econometrics.

The role of models in theory appraisal raises an important issue very little discussed in the literature. Given that a model's assumptions are *abstractions*, they are unlikely to be *exactly* true but rather, one hopes, are close *approximations* to reality.

Under these circumstances, it is important that the model's conclusions are robust with respect to small variations in its assumptions. Small variations in these assumptions should produce only small variations in its conclusions, not wild and dramatic ones. Without this robustness property empirical testing of theories becomes impossible. In fact, meaningful observations of any kind may become impossible because of 'random' environmental perturbations in the conditions under which observations are made. Consider a chemical theory which predicts the outcome of a particular chemical reaction under conditions of constant ambient temperature. Whatever care the experimental chemist takes, he will not be able to hold the ambient temperature *exactly* constant, it is bound to fluctuate slightly during the course of the experiment. Suppose now that the outcome of the experiment is substantially different from what the theory predicted. Is the theory refuted? The theoretician can always reply that the ambient temperature was not exactly constant, as his theory required, and the experiment does not therefore constitute a refutation. This would not be the case if the robustness property, discussed above, had been required of the theory *ab initio*.

This robustness property turns out to be of particular interest in the context of dynamic models: that is models in which time enters in some essential way. Such models are often constructed using the mathematics of differential and difference equations. Robustness is therefore discussed more formally in Chapters 6 and 8. Baumol (1958) notes the importance of this issue in the context of linear difference equation models of the trade cycle. Here, the problem is that persistent, regular cycles occur only for certain exact parameter values. Arbitrarily small perturbations in these parameters induce a transformation to either damped or explosive cycles. Baumol's (1958) argument is as follows:

> But our statistics are never fine enough to distinguish a unit root (of the characteristic equation of a linear difference equation) and one which takes values so close to it . . . it is usually possible to show that a slight amendment in one of the simplifying assumptions will eliminate the unit roots and so have profound qualitative effects on the system. As Solow has pointed out, since our premises are always necessarily more or less false, good theorising consists to a large extent in avoiding assumptions like these, where a small change in what is posited will seriously affect the conclusions.

As is well known, the resolution of these difficulties was eventually found by Hicks (1950), Goodwin (1951) and Desai (1973), among others, in non-linear models of the trade cycle.

Mathematical modelling then is concerned with abstraction, deduction and interpretation. The rest of this book explains various mathematical ideas which have been useful in formulating economic models. It also discusses the application of the mathematics to particular models, as well as problems of interpretation. Mathematical modelling, like mathematics, is a participatory rather than a spectator sport. The reader is urged to follow the examples through carefully and to attempt the exercises (some answers are provided in the Appendix). Having done so, he or she should feel less tempted to skip the 'nasty mathematical bit' in journal articles, and may be stimulated to construct new models, perhaps even to surpass those of the existing literature.

Further reading

Katouzian (1980), Stewart (1979) and Blaug (1980) all deal with questions of economic methodology. Much of Koopmans (1957) is concerned with the role of mathematics in economics. Popper (1959) and Kuhn (1970) are classic references on scientific methodology generally. Covick (1974) satirises model building while Leijonhufvud (1981) likens economists to a primitive tribe for whom models are sacred objects.

2 Calculus of several variables

2.1 Introduction

The purpose of this chapter is to develop certain aspects of differential calculus from the case of functions of one variable, familiar from school mathematics, to functions of several variables. Together with linear algebra, the subject of Chapter 5, differential calculus is a standard tool for the construction of models in economics and calculus methods are used in a variety of different applications in economics. A particularly large group of problems in which calculus methods manifest themselves is that class of problems involving the maximisation of some function. Edgeworth (1881) took the view that:

> The principal inquiries in Social Science may be viewed as *maximum problems*. For Economics investigates the arrangements between agents each tending to his own *maximum* utility, and Politics and (Utilitarian) Ethics investigates the arrangements which conduce to the *maximum* sum total of utility. Since, then, Social Science, as compared with the Calculus of Variations, starts from similar data – *loose quantitative relations* – and travels to a similar conclusion – determination of *maximum* – why should it not pursue the same method, Mathematics?

2.2 Functions and inverse functions

From school mathematics, the notion of a function will be familiar. Most functions the reader has dealt with have probably been real valued functions of a single real variable. Such a function (f) is often denoted:

$$f: \mathbb{R} \to \mathbb{R} \qquad (2.1)$$

An example being the function defined by:

$$f(x) = x^2 \qquad (2.2)$$

A function is a mapping from one set, D (the domain) to another, C (the codomain)

Definition 2.1

A mapping:

$$f : D \to C$$

is a *function* if: $f(x)$ exists and is unique for every $x \in D$.

Definition 2.2

The set

$$R = \{y \in C : y = f(x) \text{ for some } x \in D\}$$

is called the *range* of the function f.

Strictly speaking the specification of a function must include specification of the domain and codomain. This can be important when one is looking for the inverse of a function.

Definition 2.3

Let

$$f : D \to C$$

then an *inverse function* of f is a function denoted

$$f^{-1} : C \to D$$

such that

$$f^{-1}[f(x)] = x \text{ for all } x \in D$$

Is the function of equation (2.2) invertible? One might be tempted to specify:

$$f^{-1}(x) = \sqrt{x} \qquad (2.3)$$

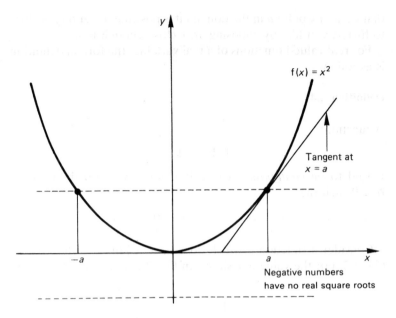

Fig. 2.1 The graph of $f(x) = x^2$.

This, however, is not a function from $\mathbb{R}$ to $\mathbb{R}$ since positive numbers have two square roots (e.g. $\sqrt{4} = \pm 2$) and negative numbers have none. This is illustrated in Fig. 2.1 which shows a graph of the function f. However, the domain and codomain of f can be respecified:

$$f : \mathbb{R}_+ \to \mathbb{R}_+ \qquad\qquad (2.4)$$

where $\mathbb{R}_+$ denotes the *positive* real numbers (including zero). Equation (2.3) *does* now specify a genuine function since every positive real number has exactly one positive square root. The graph of f with restricted domain and codomain is simply the top right-hand quadrant of Fig. 2.1.

2.3 Continuity and derivatives

The graph of f, depicted in Fig. 2.1 can be drawn without removing pen from paper. Such a function is said to be *continuous*. A continuous function is, broadly speaking, one with no jumps in it:

that is, at any point a in the domain it is possible to get f(x) as close to f(a) as you like by choosing an x close enough to a.

For real valued functions of a real variable, the formal definition is as follows.

Definition 2.4

A function:

$$f: \mathbb{R} \to \mathbb{R}$$

is said to be *continuous* at $a \in \mathbb{R}$ if for any $\varepsilon > 0$ there exists $\delta > 0$ such that

$$|x - a| < \delta \Rightarrow |f(x) - f(a)| < \varepsilon$$

Consider a function g which does have a jump, as depicted in Fig. 2.2. For the value of ε shown in Fig. 2.2 no choice of δ can be

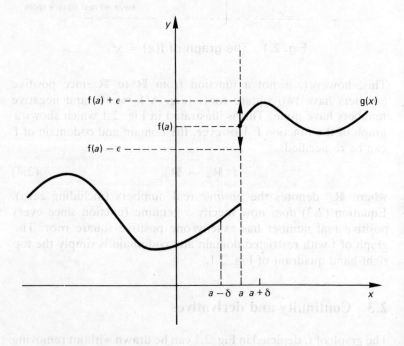

Fig. 2.2   The function g has a discontinuity at $x = a$

made to satisfy the condition of Definition 2.4. Thus the function g has a discontinuity at $x = a$. The functions one deals with in economics are typically continuous but as we will see in Chapter 8, certain kinds of discontinuities may well be important in economic models.

We now define the important notion of a *limit*. Consider a function $f: \mathbb{R} \to \mathbb{R}$ and pick a point $x_0 \in \mathbb{R}$. Now let x get closer and closer to x_0. Does there exist $l \in \mathbb{R}$ such that, as x approaches arbitrarily close to x_0, $f(x)$ approaches arbitrarily close to l? If such an l does exist it is called the limit of $f(x)$ as x tends to x_0. This is written: $l = \lim_{x \to x_0} f(x)$. The formal definition is as follows:

Definition 2.5

A function $f: \mathbb{R} \to \mathbb{R}$ is said *to approach a limit l at $x = x_0$* iff* for any $\varepsilon > 0$ there exists $\delta > 0$ such that:

$$|x - x_0| < \delta \Rightarrow |f(x) - l| < \varepsilon$$

We could now redefine continuity as follows:

Definition 2.6

A function $f: \mathbb{R} \to \mathbb{R}$ is said to be continuous at $a \in \mathbb{R}$ iff:

$$\lim_{x \to a} f(x) = f(a)$$

From school mathematics, the reader will doubtless recall the idea of *differentiation*. In Fig. 2.1 the function f clearly has a tangent at $x = a$: differentiation is the process of finding the slope of this tangent. That slope will clearly depend on the value of x at which it is calculated.

Definition 2.7

A function $f : \mathbb{R} \to \mathbb{R}$ is said to be *differentiable* at $x = a$ iff there exists a unique tangent to f at $x = a$. The slope of this tangent is called the *derivative* of f at $x = a$.

It turns out that this definition can be restated in terms of limits.

---

*The word 'iff' is used throughout the book to mean 'if and only if'.

Definition 2.8

A function $f : \mathbb{R} \to \mathbb{R}$ is said to be *differentiable* at $x = a$ if:

$$\lim_{h \to 0} \frac{f(x + h) - f(x)}{h} \qquad (h > 0)$$

and

$$\lim_{h \to 0} \frac{f(x) - f(x - h)}{h} \qquad (h > 0)$$

both exist and are equal.

The value of this limit will clearly be a function of a. It is called the *derivative* of f and is denoted f'.

Suppose we now define a variable y by: $y = f(x)$ then another notation for the derivative $f'(x)$ is dy/dx. If $f'(x)$ is itself differentiable, a new function $f''(x)$, the *second derivative* can be obtained. In some cases it is possible to differentiate a function an arbitrary number of times. The notation $f^n(x)$ represents the nth derivative of $f(x)$.

Continuity and differentiability are closely related. In fact we can state Theorem 2.1.

Theorem 2.1

A function $f : \mathbb{R} \to \mathbb{R}$ which is differentiable at $x = a$ is also continuous there.

So continuity is necessary for differentiability, but it is not sufficient. Consider the function defined by

$$f(x) = |x| \qquad (2.5)$$

(where $|x|$ denotes the absolute value of x). Its graph is shown in Fig. 2.3. The reader should be able rapidly to confirm that it is continuous at $x = 0$ but not differentiable there.

The reader will doubtless be familiar with the derivatives of certain standard functions. Some of these are reproduced below in Table 2.1.

Also familiar will be three rules for differentiating more complicated functions:

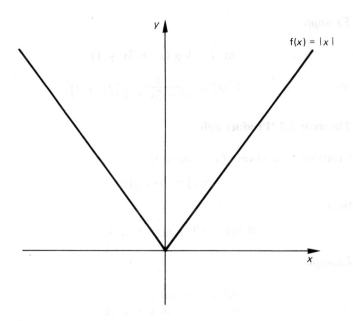

Fig. 2.3 The graph of $f(x) = |x|$.

Table 2.1 Some standard derivatives

$f(x)$	$f'(x)$
x^n	nx^{n-1}
e^x	e^x
$\log x$	$1/x$
$\sin x$	$\cos x$
$\cos x$	$-\sin x$

Theorem 2.2 (Composite function rule)

Consider a function $h(x)$ defined by:

$$h(x) = f(g(x))$$

then:

$$h'(x) = g'(x).f'(g(x))$$

Example

$$h(x) = \log (x^2 + 3x + 1)$$

$\Rightarrow$ $$h'(x) = \frac{1}{x^2 + 3x + 1} [2x + 3]$$

Theorem 2.3 (Product rule)

Consider a function $h(x)$ defined by:

$$h(x) = f(x) \cdot g(x)$$

then

$$h'(x) = f'(x) \cdot g(x) + f(x) \cdot g'(x)$$

Example

$\Rightarrow$ $$h(x) = x^2 \sin x$$
$$h'(x) = 2x \sin x + x^2 \cos x$$

Theorem 2.4 (Quotient rule)

Consider a function $h(x)$ defined by:

$$h(x) = f(x)/g(x)$$

then

$$h'(x) = \frac{f'(x) \cdot g(x) - f(x) \cdot g'(x)}{[g(x)]^2}$$

Example

$\Rightarrow$ $$h(x) = (\sin x) \, x^2$$
$$h'(x) = \frac{x^2 \cos x - 2x \sin x}{x^4}$$

It should be noted that these rules apply only *when all the relevant derivatives exist*. Consider the function

$$h(x) = |x| \cdot x \qquad (2.6)$$

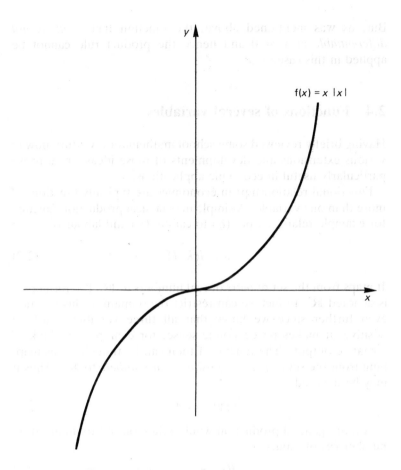

$$f(x) = x\,|x|$$

Fig. 2.4   The graph of $f(x) = x \cdot |x|$.

Its graph is shown in Fig. 2.4. The reader should easily be able to show that h has a derivative at 0 and that its value is zero. But what happens when one tries to apply the product rule?

Take

$$f(x) = |x| \quad \text{and} \quad g(x) = x$$

then

$$h(x) = f(x) \cdot g(x)$$

But, as was mentioned above, the function $f(x) = |x|$ is *not differentiable* at $x = 0$ and hence the product rule cannot be applied in this case.

2.4 Functions of several variables

Having briefly reviewed some school mathematics, we turn now to various extensions and developments of those ideas which prove particularly useful in economic applications.

Functional relationships in economics are typically functions of more than one variable. A simple neoclassical production function for example relates output (q) to capital (k) and labour (l):

$$q = f(k, l) \tag{2.7}$$

It maps from the set of *pairs* of real numbers to $\mathbb{R}$. The former set is denoted $\mathbb{R}^2$. In fact we can restrict the domain of this function even further since we know that all three variables must be positive; it makes no economic sense, for example, to think of 'negative output'. The function f then can be thought of as mapping from the set of *pairs of positive real numbers* to $\mathbb{R}_+$. Thus it may be denoted:

$$f : \mathbb{R}^2_+ \to \mathbb{R}_+ \tag{2.8}$$

A more general production would relate output to an arbitrary number (n) of inputs:

$$q = f(x_1, x_2, \ldots, x_n) \tag{2.9}$$

The list $(x_1, \ldots, x_n)$ is more readily represented by the vector notation $\mathbf{x}$. The set of all real n-vectors is denoted $\mathbb{R}^n$ and, again restricting variables to take positive values, we can write:

$$f : \mathbb{R}^n_+ \to \mathbb{R}_+ \tag{2.10}$$

Differentiating functions of several variables is a technique which is absolutely essential in many economic applications. Before turning to this question the reader might wish to consider the related question of continuity.

Exercise

Generalise the definition of 'continuity' to real-valued functions of several real variables.

The graph of a real-valued function of two real variables will of course be a two-dimensional surface in three-dimensional space. The graph of the function $z = f(x, y)$ is depicted in Fig. 2.5. At a point such as (x_0, y_0) the function has a *tangent plane* (as shown in Fig. 2.5). It is difficult then to decide how to define the derivative

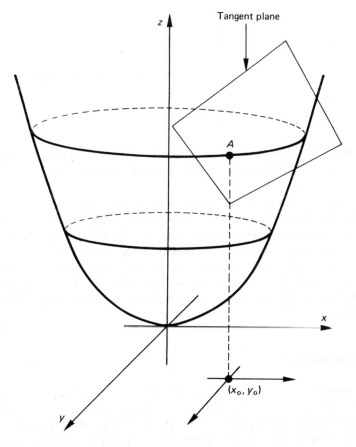

Fig. 2.5 The graph of the function $z = f(x, y)$.

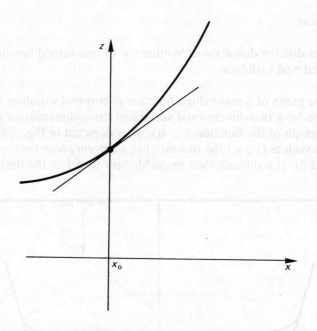

Fig. 2.6 A cross-section of the function f (depicted in Fig. 2.5) through (x_0, y_0), parallel to the x-axis.

of f because the slope of this tangent plane depends upon the *direction* in which we choose to measure it. This problem did not arise in the case of functions of one variable. What in fact is done is to choose two particular directions along which to measure the gradient of the tangent plane: namely directions parallel to the x and y axes. (This is indicated in Fig. 2.5.) The functions giving these gradients in terms of x and y are called the *partial derivatives* of f.

Definition 2.9

Consider a function: $f : \mathbb{R}^n \to \mathbb{R}$, given by the formula $y = f(\mathbf{x})$ ($\mathbf{x} = (x_1\ x_2, \ldots, x_n)$). If there exists a unique tangent plane to this function at the point $\bar{\mathbf{x}} \in \mathbb{R}^n$ then the slope of this plane in the direction of the x_i-axis is a function of $\bar{\mathbf{x}}$ and is called the *partial derivative of f with respect to* x_i. It is denoted $f_{x_i}(\bar{\mathbf{x}})$ or $f_i(\bar{\mathbf{x}})$

It should come as no surprise that partial derivatives are closely related to derivatives of functions of a single real variable. A glance at Fig. 2.5 will show that calculating the slope of the tangent plane in the x direction is equivalent to taking a cross-section of the function through (x_0, y_0) parallel to the x-axis and calculating its gradient. This is indicated in Fig. 2.6. That is to say the *partial derivative* with respect to x can be found by *holding y constant* and calculating the derivative of f *as if* it were a function of just one variable.

Theorem 2.5

Let $f : \mathbb{R}^n \to \mathbb{R}$ be a function $y = f(x_1, \ldots, x_n)$. The partial derivative $f_i(\mathbf{x})$ can be calculated by holding x_j constant where $i \neq j$ and differentiating f with respect to x_i *as if* it were a function of x_i alone.

Example

Suppose

$$f(x, y) = x^2 e^{3y}$$

Then

$$f_x = 2x e^{3y}$$

and

$$f_y = 3x^2 e^{3y}$$

It is clear that partial derivatives have some immediate economic interpretations. The neoclassical production function (equation (2.7) above) relates inputs to outputs. The partial derivative f gives a measure of how much extra output could be produced by increasing the labour input by one unit at the margin, *holding the capital input constant*. This is, of course, precisely what is meant by the *marginal product of labour*. Similarly f_k represents the marginal product of capital.

It is only possible to calculate all partial derivatives of a function if the appropriate tangent plane exists and is unique. If a unique tangent plane does not exist then the function is not differentiable.

Some non-neoclassical economists might well accept a functional relationship between inputs and outputs (at least at the level of the firm) but not accept that the relevant function is differentiable. Suppose, for example, that holes are dug by men with shovels and that there are ten men and ten shovels. *Increasing* the number of men but keeping the number of shovels constant has no effect on output. *Decreasing* the number of men, with shovels constant, will decrease output. There can therefore be no meaning to the expression 'marginal product of labour' in this case.

Exercise

Suggest a (non-differentiable) function which could be used to model the above relationship between holes, men and shovels.

Partial derivatives can often themselves be differentiated to give second, third and nth partial derivatives. These are denoted $f_{x_i x_j}$ or f_{ij} etc. . . . Neoclassical production functions are often assumed to have the property that the marginal product of a factor declines with the amount of that factor, but increases with the amount of other factors. Thus in the example discussed above it might be assumed that f_l declines with l so we can write: $f_{ll} < 0$ but increases with k : $f_{lk} > 0$.

2.5 Maxima, minima and saddlepoints

The object of this section is to develop conditions which characterise the maxima and minima of functions. This procedure provides an essential modelling tool in economics, as indicated in the quotation from Edgeworth at the beginning of this chapter. Fig. 2.7 depicts a function $f : \mathbb{R}_+ \to \mathbb{R}$. The function reaches its highest *overall* value at x_4: this is called a *global maximum*. If one is constrained to stay *near* the point x_2, however, that too is a kind of maximum: it is called a *local maximum*.

It will be familiar from school mathematics that, at points such as these the function f has a zero derivative. It is essential to take great care with this condition however: it is neither a necessary nor a sufficient condition for a maximum. The point $x = 0$ is a local maximum of f but f' is strictly *negative* there while $x = x_1$ gives a

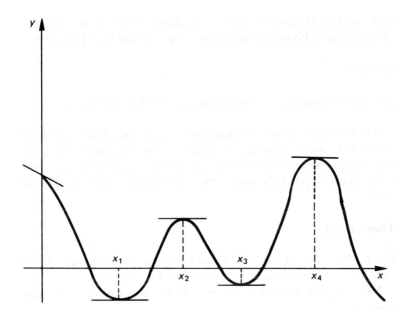

Fig. 2.7 The function $y = f(x)$ has a boundary maximum at
$x = 0$, interior maxima at $x = x_2$, x_4, and interior
minima at $x = x_1$, x_3.

zero of f' but a *minimum* of f. The point $x = 0$ gives what is called a
boundary maximum of f, the point itself being called a *boundary
point*. Note that the domain of f is $\mathbb{R}_+$, the set of positive real
numbers, including zero. Zero itself lies at the extreme edge of this
set and hence acquires the name *boundary point*. No precise
definitive of 'boundary point' is given here, since such points will be
quite self-evident in the contexts which are dealt with in the book.

Example

The closed interval $[a, b] \subset R$ has two boundary points $x = a$ and
$x = b$.

Strictly speaking the definition of a derivative (Definition 2.5)
needs to be modified if it is to apply to boundary points. But it
should be clear from Fig. 2.7 that for functions f : $\mathbb{R}_+ \to \mathbb{R}$, if

there is a local maximum at $x = 0$ then $f'(0) \leq 0$. It is equally obvious that a boundary minimum at $x = 0$ will give $f'(0) \geq 0$.

Exercise

Modify Definition 2.5 so that it applies to boundary points.

Points which are not boundary points are called *interior points* and a maximum occurring at such a point is called an *interior maximum*. For interior maxima we can safely return to the school mathematics approach concerning derivatives. In fact we can state:

Theorem 2.6

Let $f : D \to \mathbb{R}$, where $D \subset \mathbb{R}$ and suppose f attains an interior maximum or minimum at $x_0 \in D$. Then $f'(x_0) = 0$.

NB A point such as x_0, where $f'(x_0) = 0$ is called a *stationary point* of f.

So a zero derivative *is* a *necessary* condition for an interior maximum. As has already been mentioned it is not a sufficient condition because interior *minima* also have zero derivatives.

Example

Investigate the maxima and minima of the function:

$$f(x) = x^3 - \tfrac{3}{2}x^2 - 6x + 2$$
$$\Rightarrow \quad f'(x) = 3x^2 - 3x - 6 = 0$$
$$\Rightarrow \quad x^2 - x - 2 = 0$$
$$\Rightarrow \quad (x - 2)(x + 1) = 0$$
$$\Rightarrow \quad x = 2 \text{ or } -1$$

The graph of f is shown if Fig. 2.8 from which it is clear that $x = -1$ is a maximum while $x = 2$ is a minimum.

Two obvious questions arise immediately: (a) Are all stationary points maxima or minima? (b) How can we tell a maximum from a minimum without sketching the graph? To the first question the answer is definitely no. Consider, for example, the function

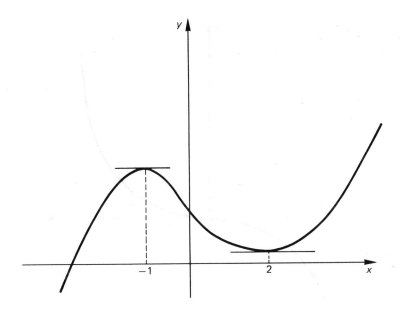

Fig. 2.8 Graph of the function $f(x) = x^3 - \frac{3}{2}x^2 - 6x + 2$.

$f(x) = x^3$ whose graph is depicted in Fig. 2.9. It evidently has a stationary point at $x = 0$ but has neither a maximum nor a minimum there. The point $x = 0$ is in fact called a *horizontal point of inflection* for this function.

The second question is one which we will not pursue here. It is in effect asking for sufficient conditions for an interior maximum or minimum. We only offer a word of warning concerning second derivatives. It is often pointed out that stationary points at which the *second* derivative is strictly negative are minima while turning points with strictly positive second derivatives are maxima.

Exercise

Check the signs of $f''(x)$ at the stationary points of the previous example where $f(x) = x^3 - \frac{3}{2}x^2 - 6x + 2$.

But what if the second derivation is zero? Surely this must be the case of a horizontal point of inflection (such as that of Fig. 2.9). Unfortunately, this is *not* the case. The reader should experiment

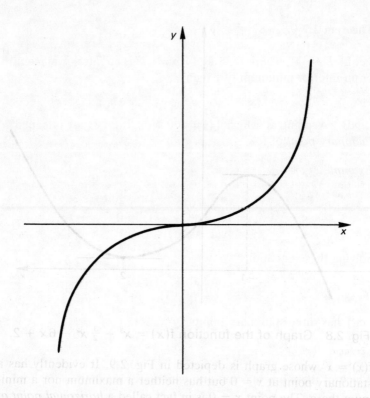

Fig. 2.9 Graph of the function $f(x) = x^3$. It has a stationary point at $x = 0$ but neither a maximum nor a minimum there.

with the function $f(x) = x^4$. Its first *and* second derivatives vanish at $x = 0$ but it has a *minimum* there, *not* a horizontal point of inflection.

The case of functions of several variables can be dealt with in a way very similar to the discussion above. The function in Fig. 2.5 clearly has an interior minimum at the origin. At this point it is clear that the tangent plane has a zero slope in *all* directions. Thus both its partial derivatives vanish there. This property can be stated as a necessary condition for an interior maximum or minimum of a function of several variables. At such a point *all* the function's partial derivatives must equal zero.

Theorem 2.7

Let $f : D \to \mathbb{R}$, where $D \subset \mathbb{R}^n$. If $\mathbf{x}_0 \in D$ is an interior maximum or an interior minimum of f then

$$f_i(\mathbf{x}_0) = 0 \qquad i = 1, \ldots, n$$

NB   A point at which $f_i(\mathbf{x}_0) = 0$ $(i = 1, \ldots, n)$ is called a *stationary point* of f.

Example

$$f(x, y) = x^4 + 4x^2y^2 - 2x^2 + 2y^2 - 1$$
$$f_x = 4x(x^2 + 2y^2 - 1) = 0$$
$$f_y = 4y(1 + 2x^2) = 0$$

Solving these equations we obtain

$$x = 0, 1, -1$$
$$y = 0$$

i.e. f has three stationary points

Exercise

Which of these are maxima and which are minima?

Horizontal points of inflection have their analogues for functions of several variables. They are called saddlepoints and they turn out to be of particular importance in economic applications. A saddlepoint is depicted in Fig. 2.10.

Definition 2.10

Let $f : D \to \mathbb{R}$, where $D \subset R^n$
If $(x_1, \ldots, x_n) \in D$ is a maximum in the direction of some of the x_i's and a minimum in the direction of the others it is called a *saddlepoint*.

Exercise

Show that the origin is a saddlepoint of f in the preceding example where $f(x, y) = x^4 + 4x^2y^2 - 2x^2 + 2y^2 - 1$

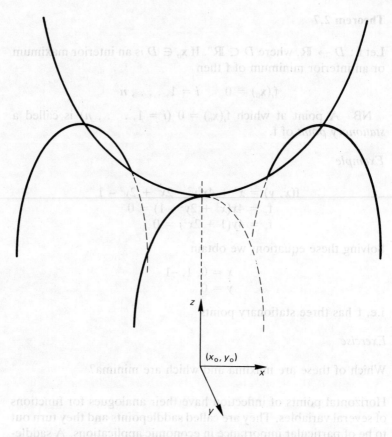

Fig. 2.10 A saddlepoint. At the point (x_0, y_0) f has a
minimum in the x direction but a maximum
in the y direction.

2.6 Convexity and Concavity

Sufficient conditions for maxima and minima of functions of several variables can be stated. Not surprisingly they involve second partial derivatives. We do not take that course here, though the reader will find discussions of these sufficient (or 'second-order') conditions in Chiang (1984).

Instead we adopt a slightly different approach which proves parti-

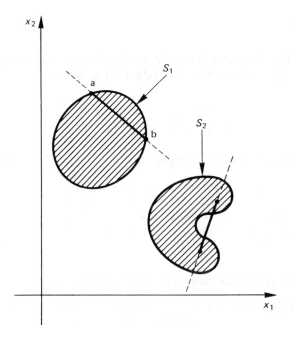

Fig. 2.11 The set $S_1 \subset \mathbb{R}^2$ is convex while the set
$S_2 \subset \mathbb{R}^2$ is not.

cularly fruitful in economic applications. Consider a set $S_1 \subset \mathbb{R}^2$
such as the one depicted in Fig. 2.11. The set S_1 'bulges outwards'
everywhere. That is to say, given any two points $\mathbf{a}$, $\mathbf{b} \in S_1$ the line
segment joining them also lies entirely in S_1. The set S_1 is said to be
convex. Note that this is not true of the set S_2. The line segment
joining $\mathbf{a}$ and $\mathbf{b}$ can be generated by taking linear combinations of $\mathbf{a}$
and $\mathbf{b}$. It is simply the set of points such as $\mathbf{c}$, where:

$$\mathbf{c} = \lambda\mathbf{a} + (1 - \lambda)\mathbf{b} \qquad (0 \leqslant \lambda \leqslant 1) \qquad (2.10)$$

Definition 2.11

Let $S \subset \mathbb{R}^n$. S is *convex* if, for all $\mathbf{a}$, $\mathbf{b} \in S$, $\lambda\mathbf{a} + (1 - \lambda)\mathbf{b} \in S$
(for all λ: $0 \leqslant \lambda \leqslant 1$).

Example

Suppose a consumer has a money budget m and faces prices $p_1, \ldots, p_n$ for n goods. His budget set is the set:

$$B = \{(x_1, \ldots, x_n) \in \mathbb{R}^n : \\ p_1 x_1 + p_2 x_2 + \cdots + p_n x_n \leqslant m\} \quad (2.11)$$

B is convex. Let $\mathbf{x}, \mathbf{y} \in B$ then

$$\left. \begin{array}{c} p_1 x_1 + \cdots + p_n x_n \leqslant m \\ p_1 y_1 + \cdots + p_n y_n \leqslant m \end{array} \right\} \quad (2.12)$$

$$\Rightarrow \left\{ \begin{array}{c} \lambda p_1 x_1 + \cdots + \lambda p_n x_n \leqslant m \\ (1-\lambda) p_1 y_1 + \cdots + (1-\lambda) p_n y_n \leqslant (1-\lambda) m \end{array} \right\} \; (0 \leqslant \lambda \leqslant 1) \quad (2.13)$$

Adding these two inequalities (and rearranging):

$$p_1(\lambda x_1 + (1-\lambda) y_1) + \cdots + p_n(\lambda x_n + (1-\lambda) y_n) \leqslant m \quad (2.14)$$

$$\Rightarrow \qquad \lambda \mathbf{x} + (1 - \lambda)\mathbf{y} \in B \quad (2.15)$$

and B is convex.

Exercise

Consider a firm producing output y using inputs $x_1, \ldots, x_n$. Let Y be set of points $(y, x_1, \ldots, x_n)$ which the firm can produce; its production set. Show that convexity of Y corresponds to diminishing (or constant) returns to scale.

It is now possible to define a *concave* function. Such a function is simply one which bounds a convex set. In Fig. 2.12 are depicted two functions, f and g mapping a convex set S to the real line. The function f which 'bends outwards everywhere' is concave while the function g is not. We can formalise this 'bending outwards' property by considering two arbitrary points a and b in the set S. If we take a particular linear combination c of a and b a concave function will have the property that f(c) will be greater than (or equal to) to the same linear combination of f(a) and f(b). This is illustrated in Fig. 2.12 and formalised in Definition 2.12.

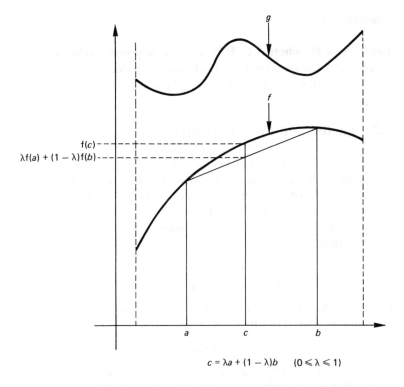

$$c = \lambda a + (1 - \lambda)b \qquad (0 \leqslant \lambda \leqslant 1)$$

Fig. 2.12   The function f is concave while the function g is not.

Definition 2.12

Let $f : S \to \mathbb{R}$, where $S \subset \mathbb{R}^n$ is convex. f is said to be *concave* if for any $\mathbf{a}, \mathbf{b} \in S$:

$$f(\lambda \mathbf{a} + (1 - \lambda)\mathbf{h}) \geqslant \lambda f(\mathbf{a}) + (1 - \lambda)\, f(\mathbf{b})$$

(for all λ: $0 \leqslant \lambda \leqslant 1$)

  NB   The domain of f must be assumed convex otherwise we could not be sure that $\mathbf{c} = \lambda \mathbf{a} + (1 - \lambda)\mathbf{b}$ is an element of S. If it is not then $f(c)$ makes no sense.

  Concave functions have the useful property that the conditions discussed above as *necessary* for a maximum are both necessary and sufficient for an interior maximum of a concave function.

Theorem 2.8

Let $f : S \to \mathbb{R}$, where $S \subset \mathbb{R}^n$ is convex. Suppose f to be concave. Then $\mathbf{x} \in S$ (assumed not to be a boundary point of S) is a global interior maximum of f if and only if $f_i(\mathbf{x}) = 0$ $(i = 1, \ldots, n)$.

2.7 Partial and total derivatives

It is often the case in economics that one is dealing with situations where one variable is a function of several others which themselves can be thought of as functions of yet another variable. The most common case of this kind of relationship is the one in which this last variable is time. Consider an aggregate neoclassical production function:

$$Y = F(K, L) \tag{2.16}$$
$$Y = \text{output}, \; K = \text{capital} \; L = \text{labour}$$

In growth theory we are interested in how these variables change over time and we typically think of each one as a function of time

$$Y(t) = F(K(t), L(t)) \tag{2.17}$$

How can we now obtain an expression for the growth rate of Y? It is here that we can utilise the following theorem which relates total and partial derivatives.

Theorem 2.9

Let $f : D \to \mathbb{R}$, where $D \subset \mathbb{R}^n$
Suppose $\mathbf{x} \in \mathbb{R}^n$ is such that $x_i = x_i(t)$ $(i = 1, \ldots, n)$ where t is a real variable. Then $f'(t) = f_1 x_1'(t) + f_2 x_2'(t) \ldots f_n x_n'(t)$
NB $f'(t)$ is sometimes called a *total derivative* of f to distinguish it from f_i $(i = 1, \ldots, n)$, the partial derivatives.

Example

For the neoclassical aggregate production function above, how can we obtain an expression for the growth rate of output? First note that the standard notation for derivatives with respect to time is $Y'(t) = \dot{Y}$.

Consider the particular case of a Cobb–Douglas production function:

$$Y(t) = A\ K^{\alpha}(t)\ .\ L^{\beta}(t) \qquad (2.18)$$

$$\Rightarrow \quad \dot{Y} = A[Y_K.\dot{K} + Y_L.\dot{L}] \qquad \text{(by Theorem 2.9)} \qquad (2.19)$$

$$= A[\alpha K^{\alpha-1}L^{\beta}.\dot{K} + \beta K^{\alpha}L^{\beta-1}\dot{L}] \qquad (2.20)$$

$$\Rightarrow \quad \frac{\dot{Y}}{Y} = \frac{\alpha K^{\alpha-1}L^{\beta}.\dot{K}}{K^{\alpha}L^{\beta}} + \frac{\beta K^{\alpha}L^{\beta-1}.\dot{L}}{K^{\alpha}L^{\beta}} \qquad (2.21)$$

$$= \frac{\alpha \dot{K}}{K} + \frac{\beta \dot{L}}{L} \qquad (2.22)$$

Using the notation $\hat{X} = \dot{X}/X$ for proportional rates of growth, we have

$$\hat{Y} = \alpha\hat{K} + \beta\hat{L} \qquad (2.23)$$

This equation gives the (proportional) growth rate of output in terms of the production function parameters and the (proportional) growth rates of the factors.

Exercises

1 Let f: $[1, 4] \to \mathbb{R}$ be defined by $f(x) = 5 + 3x$. What is the *range* of f?

2 Sketch graphs of the functions defined by the following equations:

(i) $f(x) = x^2 + 4x - 2$
(ii) $f(x) = 1/x$. What is the domain of this function?
(iii) $f(x) = \sin x$ What are the domain and range of this function. Does it have an inverse?

3 Define the *hyperbolic functions* as follows:
$$\left.\begin{array}{l} \sinh x = \tfrac{1}{2}(e^x - e^{-x}) \\ \cosh x = \tfrac{1}{2}(e^x + e^{-x}) \\ \tanh x = \dfrac{\sinh x}{\cosh x} \end{array}\right\} \quad x \in \mathbb{R}$$

(i) Find the derivative of tanh x.

(ii) Sketch graphs of the three hyperbolic functions defined above. What are their ranges and domains. Are they invertible?

(iii) Show that the inverse of cosh x is given by:
$$\cosh^{-1} x = \pm \log (x + \sqrt{x^2 - 1})$$

4 For the CES production function:

$$Y = (aK^{-\beta} + bL^{-\beta})^{-1/\beta} \qquad (a, b, > 0 \; \beta \neq 0)$$

find the marginal products of capital and labour.

5 Find all the stationary points of the function

$$f(x, y) = x^3 + xy + y^2$$

6 Give an example of a subset of $\mathbb{R}^2$ which is not convex *and* does not have a convex complement.

7 Are the following functions concave?

(i) $f(x) = \log x$
(ii) $g(x) = \sin x \quad$ ($g:[0, \pi] \to [-1, 1]$)
(iii) $h(x, y) = x^\alpha y^\beta \quad (0 < \alpha, \beta, < 1)$

8 Give an example of a *non-concave* function $f : \mathbb{R}^2 \to \mathbb{R}$ such that every set of the form:

$$S_k = \{(x, y) \in \mathbb{R}^2 : f(x, y) \geq k\} \qquad (k \in \mathbb{R})$$

in convex. Can you think of an economic interpretation of sets such as S_k?

Further reading

There are countless mathematics textbooks which discuss functions and differential calculus. Baumol (1977) provides a useful discussion of calculus methods as does Chiang (1984).

3 Kuhn–Tucker theory

3.1 Introduction

In Chapter 2 the maximisation and minimisation of real-valued functions was discussed in some detail. In this chapter, this theme is developed in a way which has proved of major significance in economics. Economists frequently model behaviour by assuming that some agent in maximising (or possibly, minimising) some well-defined objective function, subject to a number of constraints. Consumers are supposed to maximise their 'utility', subject to a budget constraint. Firms might be assumed to maximise their growth rate subject to a lower limit on profits. Governments' behaviour is sometimes modelled as the maximisation of a 'social welfare function' subject to the behavioural constraints of economic agents. In a sense, constrained maximisation has come to represent a kind of paradigm, namely that of *rational* behaviour. It can be shown for example (see Debreu, 1959), that a rational agent with a certain type of consistent preference will behave as if he or she were maximising a continuous utility function.

It is not usually clear in economics whether agents are supposed to be making *conscious* maximising choices or whether these choices emerge in some other way. Consider a useful analogy from another discipline: Biology. One might well model photosynthesising plants by assuming that they arrange their leaves so as to maximise exposure to light, subject to various physical constraints. Such a model will frequently predict reasonably accurately the disposition of a plant's leaves but clearly no one would assert that the plant had made any conscious choices.

Returning to economics, firms are frequently assumed to maximise profits subject to technological and market constraints. It may be that firms carefully analyse their cost and demand structures in order to make profit-maximising choices, but this would require a considerable computational effort. On the other hand, it may be that profit-maximising emerges through a kind of 'natural selection', with the unsuccessful maximisers forced out of the market by the process of competition (see Nelson and Winter, 1982). Thus maximising models in economics are often based on the assumption that an agent behaves *as if* he were maximising an objective subject to constraints, even if his maximising choices are not supposed to be made consciously.

The important mathematical point to grasp is that models of the type discussed above rely heavily on a precise restriction of the domain of the objective function. Agents are assumed not to have a choice of *any* value in the function's domain, but rather to choose from a subset of that domain. It is frequently important to analyse the consequences for the agent's choices, of changes in the constraints. As constraints change, the subset from which the maximising choice is made will change. In general one would expect this to lead to a change in the agents' choices. Thus a price rise will shrink the consumer's budget set, leading to a new choice of consumption vector. One would normally expect continuous changes in the constraints to lead to continuous changes in choices, but this is not always the case, as will be discussed in Chapter 8.

3.2 Constrained maximisation and minimisation

The models discussed in this chapter have the mathematical form of constrained maximisation or minimisation problems. Minimising a function $F(\mathbf{x})$ can be thought of as maximising $-F(\mathbf{x})$, so attention will be focused on maximisation. The function to be maximised will be a real valued function of n real variables: $f: \mathbb{R}^n \to \mathbb{R}$. This function will be called the *objective function or maximand*. The constraints, k in number, will be expressed as *inequalities* so that the mathematical problem to be solved is;

$$\left.\begin{array}{ll} \text{Maximise: } f(\mathbf{x}) & (\mathbf{x} = (x_1, \ldots, x_n) \in \mathbb{R}^n) \\ \text{subject to: } g_i(\mathbf{x}) \geq 0 & (i = 1, 2, \ldots, k) \end{array}\right\} \quad (3.1)$$

The functions $g_i(x)$ will be called the *constraint functions*. A vector satisfying the constraints in (3.1) will be called a *feasible vector*, and a feasible vector which maximises f(**x**) will be called an *optimum*.

It is important to note the *in*equality form of the constraints. This is usually the appropriate form for economic models. Consumers, for example, are supposed to maximise a utility function subject to the constraint that their expenditure *does not exceed* their budget. A consumer's expenditure may conceivably be *less* than the available budget but it cannot be more. If a constraint holds with equality: $g_i(\mathbf{x}) = 0$, it is said to be *binding*, if it holds with strict inequality: $g_i(\mathbf{x}) > 0$, it is said to be *slack*. It often proves to be of interest to ascertain the conditions under which an optimum for (3.1) gives rise to binding or slack constraints.

3.3 Kuhn–Tucker methods

Definition 3.1

Let $\lambda_1, \ldots, \lambda_k \geq 0$ be real variables. Denote $(\lambda_1, \ldots, \lambda_k)$ by λ. Then the function

$$L(\mathbf{x}, \lambda) = f(\mathbf{x}) + \lambda_1 g_1(\mathbf{x}) + \lambda_2 g_2(\mathbf{x}) + \cdots + \lambda_k \, g_k(\mathbf{x}) \quad (3.2)$$

is called the *Lagrangian* for the problem (3.1)

Note that there is a λ_i for each constraint $g_i(x)$; the λ_i's are called *multipliers* or *shadow prices*. The reason for these mathematical entities to have such an economic sounding name will be discussed later in the chapter.

Definition 3.2

A vector $(\mathbf{x}^*, \lambda^*)$ which is a maximum of $L(\mathbf{x}, \lambda)$ with respect to each x_i $(i = 1, \ldots, n)$ and a minimum with respect to each λ_j $(j = 1, \ldots, k)$ is called a *solution* of the Lagrangian $L(\mathbf{x}, \lambda)$. (Note that a solution of a Lagrangian is, in the terminology of Chapter 2, a special kind of saddlepoint.)

We now turn to the central theorems of this chapter.

Theorem 3.1

Let, f, $g_1, \ldots, g_k$ be concave (and hence have a convex domain $X \subset \mathbb{R}^n$). Suppose also that there exists $\bar{x} \in X$ such that $g_j(\bar{x}) > 0$ for all $j = 1, \ldots, k$. Then x^* is an optimum for problem 3.1 if and only if there exists $\lambda^* \in \mathbb{R}_+^k$ (hence $\lambda^* \geqslant 0$) such that (x^*, λ^*) is a solution of the Lagrangian.

The condition that there exists $\bar{x} \in \mathbb{R}^n$ such that $g_j(\bar{x}) > 0$ for all $j = 1, \ldots, k$ is called Slater's condition. It requires simply that the constraints of problem (3.1) be such that it is possible for them all to be slack simultaneously.

Now suppose, in addition, that the functions f and $g_1, \ldots, g_k$ are differentiable, but impose the extra condition that their domain X is the whole of $\mathbb{R}^n$. We can now characterise an optimum of (3.1) (which, by Theorem 3.1, is the same thing as a solution of the Lagrangian) by calculus methods. This is simply a matter of looking for a maximum of the Lagrangian with respect to each x_i and a minimum with respect to each λ_j, remembering that $\lambda \geqslant 0$. Such a characterisation is provided by:

Theorem 3.2

Let f, $g_1, \ldots, g_k$ be concave and differentiable, with the whole of $\mathbb{R}^n$ as domain. Assume Slater's condition is satisfied (i.e. there exists $\bar{x} \in \mathbb{R}^n$ such that $g_j(\bar{x}) > 0$ for $j = 1, \ldots, k$). Then, x^* is an optimum for problem 3.1 if and only if there exists $\lambda^* \geqslant 0$ such that:

(a′) $L_{x_i}(x^*, \lambda^*) = 0 \qquad i = 1, \ldots, n$
(b′) $\lambda_j^* \cdot g_j(x^*) = 0 \qquad j = 1, \ldots, k$

Note that Slater's condition is an assumption of this theorem as well as of Theorem 3.1. In fact it is required only to make the saddlepoint characterisation *necessary* for an optimum. It is not required to make it *sufficient*.

It is often the case in economic modelling that non-negativity conditions are imposed on the choice variables of a maximising problem. That is, we frequently require $x \geqslant 0$ in problem (3.1). If, for example, x represents a firm's choice of output and input levels it would be meaningless to allow x to have negative components. This situation could be dealt with by restricting the domains of the functions f, $g_1, \ldots, g_k$ to $\mathbb{R}_+^n$, but this would violate a condition of Theorem 3.2. However, Theorem 3.1 remains valid since it requires only that f, $g_1, \ldots, g_k$ have a convex domain in $\mathbb{R}^n$ and, of course, $\mathbb{R}_+^n$ is convex. The problem then is to characterise a saddlepoint which may occur at a boundary point of the domain of f. This is achieved by the following theorem. An alternative approach would be to introduce extra constraints $x_1 \geqslant 0$, $x_2 \geqslant 0, \ldots, x_n \geqslant 0$ and rewrite the Lagrangian. This, of course, produces the same result. We have then:

Theorem 3.3

Let f, $g_1, \ldots, g_k$, be concave and differentiable. Impose the restriction $\mathbf{x} \geqslant \mathbf{0}$ so that f, $g_1, \ldots, g_k$ have $\mathbb{R}_+^n$ as domain. Assume Slater's condition is satisfied (i.e. assume there exists $\bar{\mathbf{x}} \in R_+^n$ such that $g_j(\bar{\mathbf{x}}) > 0$ for $j = 1, \ldots, k$). Then $\mathbf{x}^* \geqslant 0$ is an optimum for problem (3.1) if and only if there exists $\boldsymbol{\lambda}^* \geqslant \mathbf{0}$ such that:

(a) $L_{x_i}(\mathbf{x}^*, \boldsymbol{\lambda}^*) \leqslant 0 \qquad i = 1, \ldots, n$
(b) $x_i^* \cdot L_{x_i}(\mathbf{x}^*, \boldsymbol{\lambda}^*) = 0 \qquad i = 1, \ldots, n$
(c) $\lambda_j^* \cdot g_j(\mathbf{x}^*) = 0 \qquad j = 1, \ldots, k$

Requirements (a), (b) and (c) in Theorem 3.3 are sometimes referred to as the Kuhn–Tucker conditions. Condition (b) requires that either a state variable x_i be zero *or* the derivative of the Lagrangian with respect to x_i be zero. Condition (c) (or (b') in Theorem 3.2) is sometimes called the complementary slackness condition. It requires that, at an optimum *either* a constraint is binding *or* its multiplier is zero (or possibly both).

The original Kuhn–Tucker approach (Kuhn and Tucker, 1951) was slightly different from that adopted above, in that they derived the Kuhn–Tucker conditions as necessary, though not sufficient, for an optimum. They did not, however, impose the concavity requirement on the functions f, $g_1, \ldots, g_k$, but did impose an extra condition, known as the Kuhn–Tucker constraint qualification, on the functions $g_1, \ldots, g_k$. This condition is rather difficult to check and has no obvious economic interpretation. Slater's condition, which partially substitutes for the constraint qualification in the above treatment, is relatively mild and may readily be imposed in most economic applications.

3.4 An application of Kuhn–Tucker methods

Consider a firm of the type discussed by Baumol (1967). It produces a single output Q and its sales are affected by advertising, so that its revenue, R, is affected by its choice of output and its level of advertising expenditure, A. That is;

$$R = R(Q, A)$$

Suppose $1 > R_A > 0$ and that the firm's production costs are given by

$$C = C(Q)$$

with $C_Q > 0$. Assume that the firm is attempting to maximise its revenue subject to the constraint that its profits (Π) do not fall below a certain minimum m. Baumol calls this *satisficing* behaviour.

Theorem 3.3 provides a means of modelling this type of firm. The firm's profits are given by:

$$\Pi = R(Q, A) - C(Q) - A \tag{3.3}$$

It is attempting to:

Maximise: $R(Q, A)$

subject to: $\left.\begin{array}{l} \Pi = R(Q, A) - C(Q) - A \geq m \\ \Leftrightarrow R(Q, A) - C(Q) - A - m \geq 0 \end{array}\right\} \tag{3.4}$

(Expressing the constraint in the form of problem (3.1).)
Form the Lagrangian, by taking a multiplier $\lambda \geq 0$ for the profit constraint:

$$L(Q, A, \lambda) = R(Q, A) + \lambda[R(Q, A) - C(Q) - A - m] \tag{3.5}$$

Assume the conditions of Theorem 3.3 are satisfied, and suppose that $Q, A > 0$, for otherwise the firm's behaviour would be uninteresting. Then the Kuhn–Tucker conditions of Theorem 3.3 can be applied as follows:

$$L_Q = 0 \Leftrightarrow R_Q + \lambda[R_Q - C_Q] = 0 \tag{3.6}$$
$$L_A = 0 \Leftrightarrow R_A + \lambda[R_A - 1] = 0 \tag{3.7}$$

Then:

$$\lambda = R_A/(1 - R_A) \text{ (from (3.7))} \tag{3.8}$$
$$\Rightarrow \lambda > 0 \text{ since } 0 < R_A < 1$$

The multiplier λ is strictly positive and hence, by condition (c) of Theorem 3.3, the corresponding constraint must bind. Thus: $\Pi = m$, *and the firm earns its minimum profit, m*

From equation (3.6) we have:

$$R_Q = \left(\frac{\lambda}{1+\lambda}\right)C_Q \qquad (3.9)$$

Since $\lambda > 0$ and $C_Q > 0$ it follows that $R_Q > 0$, i.e. the firm's marginal revenue is strictly positive. For an unconstrained revenue maximiser we would have $R_Q = 0$.

How does the firm compare with a straightforward profit-maximiser? We have

$$\Pi = R(Q, A) - C(Q) - A$$
$$\Rightarrow \qquad \Pi_Q = R_Q - C_Q$$
$$= \left[\frac{-1}{1+\lambda}\right]C_Q < 0 \qquad (3.10)$$

(from (3.9) since $\lambda > 0$, $C_Q > 0$)

A pure profit-maximiser would have $\Pi_Q = 0$

Exercise

Show that, with 'normal' marginal revenue and cost curves, the satisficer's output is greater than the profit-maximiser's but less than the unconstrained revenue maximiser's.

The assumption was made that $0 < R_A < 1$. What would happen if $R_A > 1$? Then equation (3.8) implies that $\lambda < 0$, which is impossible. In this case, no optimum exists. The economic reason is obvious: with $R_A > 1$ the firm would seek to increase its advertising expenditure indefinitely, for it could always increase revenue without reducing profits.

3.5 Multipliers as shadow prices

The multipliers of Definition 3.1 have an important economic interpretation. It can be shown (see Dixit (1976), for further discussion) that at a solution of the Lagrangian, each multiplier has a value which is equal to the amount that the objective function could be increased if the corresponding constraint were relaxed by a 'marginal' unit. The multiplier thus represents a *shadow price*, giving the agent's private valuation of a constraint in terms of his own objectives. Consider for example a profit-maximising firm constrained by the Government not to produce more than 1 million units of pollution every year: the firm faces a pollution constraint. The multiplier (or shadow price) on that constraint is the maximum that the firm would be willing to pay to bribe an official to allow it to produce one extra unit of pollution. In the special type of optimising problem where objective and constraint functions are linear (linear programmes) shadow prices can be calculated relatively easily. This will be done in Chapter 4.

Note that this interpretation of the multiplier is consistent with clause (c) of theorem 3.3. If a constraint is slack it must have a zero multiplier. To put it another way, if a constraint does not impinge on the agent's behaviour, he or she will accord it a shadow price of zero.

There are some startling implications of this view of multipliers. Suppose that there exist many unemployed coal-miners and that a pit is undergoing a cost–benefit analysis. To society as a whole the labour constraint is slack and thus should be accorded a zero shadow price, making shadow social labour costs equal to zero. Such a view would suggest keeping open a far greater number of pits than is usually held to be appropriate.

The next section develops a model of the 'labour-managed firm' which, among other things, will illustrate the interpretation of multipliers as shadow prices.

3.6 Modelling the labour-managed firm

A considerable literature exists about firms in which management decisions are taken by the workforce in some democratic way. Perhaps they are workers' cooperatives, worker-owned firms or labour-managed firms of Yugoslav type. (See, for example Vanek (1970), Stephen (1982), Jones and Svejnar (1982) and George (1982) for further discussion.) In such firms labour is the hiring not the hired factor and a standard assumption on the firm's behaviour is that it maximises, not profits, but income per worker.

Consider such a firm producing an output (X) using labour (N) and capital (K) subject to the production function:

$$X \leq F(N, K)$$
$$\Leftrightarrow F(N, K) - X \geq 0 \qquad (3.11)$$

The firm sells its output at a fixed price (p) and rents its capital (perhaps from the State) at a fixed rental (r). Such a firm closely resembles the textbook firm, but has a different maximand. How does its equilibrium differ from that of the standard textbook firm, and, in particular, do labour and capital receive their marginal value products?

Income per worker (R) is given by:

$$R = \frac{pX - rK}{N} \qquad (3.12)$$

(We assume all workers to supply the same amount of labour.)

The firm is seeking to maximise (3.12) subject to the constraint (3.11). Taking a multiplier λ for the constraint, the Lagrangian is:

$$L(X, N, K, \lambda) = \frac{pK - rK}{N} + \lambda[F(N, K) - X] \qquad (3.13)$$

Now, suppose $X, N, K > 0$ and apply the conditions of Theorem 3.3:

$$L_X = \frac{p}{L} - \lambda = 0 \qquad (3.14)$$

$$L_N = -\frac{(pX - rK)}{N^2} + \lambda F_N = 0 \qquad (3.15)$$

$$L_K = \frac{-r}{N} + \lambda F_K = 0 \qquad (3.16)$$

Equation (3.14) gives;

$$\lambda = \frac{p}{N} \qquad (3.17)$$

Note that this confirms the interpretation of multipliers given in Section 3.5. If the firm's production function were relaxed so that it could produce one more marginal unit of output, this could be sold for a price p, increasing income per worker by p/N.

If $p > 0$ then $\lambda > 0$ and, appealing to condition (c) of Theorem 3.3, this tells us that the firm's production function constraint is binding.

Substituting (3.17) into (3.15) gives:

$$\frac{pF_N}{N} = \frac{pX - rK}{N^2}$$

$$\Rightarrow \qquad\qquad R = pF_N \qquad \text{(from (3.12))} \qquad\qquad (3.18)$$

So labour certainly does receive its marginal value product. Substituting (3.17) into (3.16) gives:

$$\frac{pF_K}{N} = \frac{r}{N}$$

$$\Rightarrow \qquad\qquad r = pF_K \qquad\qquad\qquad\qquad (3.19)$$

so capital also receives its marginal value product. This does not necessarily mean that the equilibria of the labour-managed and profit maximising firms are identical however.

Exercise

Show that the labour-managed firm will, in equilibrium, have a higher capital/labour ratio than a profit-maximising firm making positive profits. (Assume both firms face the same prices p and r and have the same production functions.)

Exercises

1 Consider a profit-maximising firm facing given prices p_1 in the high season and p_2 in the low season. High and low season outputs are q_1 and q_2 respectively. The maximum output level is y, this being produced *only* in the high season. Annual operating costs are given by $C(q_1, q_2)$ and annual capital costs $K(y)$.

   (a) Set up the firm's profit-maximising problem in Kuhn–Tucker form.
   (b) Hence, or otherwise, show:
      (i) that low season prices will just cover marginal operating costs
      (ii) high season prices will exceed marginal operating cost by an amount equal to marginal capital cost.
      (you may assume $y, q_1, q_2 > 0$)

(c) How useful is this model in analysing peak-pricing policies for telephone calls or electricity?

2 A profit maximising firm produces an output Y, using a resource R and labour l, subject to a concave production function:

$$Y \leqslant f(R, l)$$

A government rationing scheme imposes an upper limit R_0 to the amount of the resource the firm may use. The firm sells output (Y) and buys inputs (R and l) at fixed prices.

(i) Express the firm's profit maximisation problem in Kuhn–Tucker form and show that labour receives its marginal value product.

(ii) Show further that the multiplier on the resource constraint is equal to the extra profit the firm could derive from receiving a marginal unit of the resource.

3 A firm produces an output Q using two inputs, X and Y, which it purchases at prices u and v respectively. The firm has production function

$$Q \leqslant X^\alpha Y^\beta \qquad (\alpha + \beta = \gamma < 1)$$

The firm's cost function is defined by

$$C(Q : u, v) = \text{Min } (uX + vY)$$

subject to the constraint

$$Q \leqslant X^\alpha Y^\beta$$

By using Kuhn–Tucker methods, or otherwise, show that the firm's cost function is given by

$$C(Q : u, v) = \gamma Q^{1/\gamma} \left(\frac{u}{\alpha}\right)^{\alpha/\gamma} \left(\frac{v}{\beta}\right)^{\beta/\gamma}$$

What would happen if there were constant returns to scale in production?

4 Consider a firm producing a single output q. The firm faces a demand curve:

$$p = a - bq + dx \qquad (a, b, d \text{ positive constants})$$

where x = marketing expenditure. The firm's production cost function is $C(q)$. It seeks to maximise total marketed output (q) subject to the constraints:

(a) the ratio of price to average *total* cost (i.e. including marketing costs) does not fall below a minimum k;

(b) a constraint imposed upon the firm by a cartel it has joined that marketing costs must not exceed a fraction m (< 1) of total costs.

   (i) Set up the firm's optimisation problem in Kuhn-Tucker form.

   (ii) Derive the Kuhn-Tucker conditions for an optimum. Hence, or otherwise show that if $d > k$ then: constraint (b) must bind though constraint (a) need not do so.

5 Consider a consumer facing a budget constraint and a leisure time constraint. Suppose one unit of each good requires one hour of leisure time for its consumption and that the consumer has 10 hours of leisure time altogether. He therefore faces a time constraint;

$$X_1 + X_2 \leqslant 10$$

where X_i = quantity of good i consumed ($i = 1, 2$).
Let the consumer have the utility function:

$$u(X_1, X_2) = X_1 X_2$$

and a budget of £12. Suppose he faces prices of £1 and £2 for goods 1 and 2 respectively.

  (i) Find the optimal quantities of both goods and the shadow prices of both the consumer's constraints.

  (ii) Would the consumer benefit from a tax on his income used to increase his leisure time?

6 Let q_1 and q_2 be the outputs of a firm during the winter and summer respectively. The firm faces revenue functions $R_1(q_1)$ and $R_2(q_2)$ in the two seasons and an annual cost function $C(q_1, q_2)$. Suppose that the firm seeks to maximise total output subject to the constraint that profits per unit of output do not fall below a minimum, m.

(a) Set up the firm's problem in Kuhn–Tucker form.

(b) Suppose $R_1' < 0$, $R_2' > 0$ and $C_1 = C_2$

Prove that the firm earns its minimum profit per unit of output and that it produces no output in the winter.

7 A country exports a good X and imports a good M. Normalise the price (domestic and world) of X to unity and take it and the exchange rate as fixed. Let p = domestic price of imports and q = world price of imports. A government ministry imposes a tariff at rate t so that

$$p = (1 + t)\, q$$

It can also increase the country's exports by spending an amount B on a promotion campaign, so that

$$X = X(B)$$

and you may assume $X' = \beta > 0$, where β is a constant. You may also assume a demand curve for imports:

$$M = p^\alpha \qquad (\alpha < -1)$$

The ministry wishes to choose the tariff rate t and its promotional expenditure B to maximise

$$tqM - B$$

the difference between its income from tariff revenue and its expenditure on export promotion.

It is subject to the constraint that the balance of trade $(X - qM)$ must not be negative. (You may assume throughout that $t, B > 0$.)

(i) Set up the problem in Kuhn–Tucker form
(ii) Show that the balance of trade is exactly equal to zero
(iii) Show that:

$$qM\left(1 + \frac{\alpha t}{1 + t} - \frac{\alpha}{\beta\,(1 + t)}\right) = 0$$

Further reading

Utility theory is discussed at length by Green (1976). Baumol (1977) and Chiang (1984) contain discussions of constrained optimisation. Dixit (1976) is devoted entirely to optimisation methods and their application in economics. Dixit's treatment is reasonably advanced, though his notation can be rather opaque. Intrilligator

(1971) also provides a moderately advanced discussion of optimisation.

Baumol (1967) discusses 'satisficing' behaviour of firms, and Simon (1959, 1967) and Cyert and March (1963) interpret it as part of a 'behavioural' theory of the firm.

Vanek (1970) is the classic reference on the theory of the labour-managed economy. See also Ireland and Law (1982). Jones and Svejnar (1982) and Stephen (1982) contain some interesting empirical material on self-management and George (1982) reviews some of the issues in this area.

4 Linear programming

4.1 Introduction

In this chapter we turn to a special case of the constrained optimisation problem discussed in Chapter 3. It is the case in which the objective and constraint functions are all *linear*. Such problems are called *linear programmes* and are probably the commonest kind of model in practical applications of economics. The linear nature of these problems admits the use of *matrix* notation which will be familiar from school mathematics (any reader requiring a reminder on elementary matrix ideas should consult Chiang, 1984).

In practice the solving of large linear programmes is undertaken by computers which can accomplish this mechanical task within fractions of a second. In order to write a computer program to achieve this one must develop a numerical algorithm (or routine), which provides the basis for the computer's calculations. Such algorithms are discussed briefly in Section 4.5, though the bulk of the chapter is concerned with the *theory* of linear programming.

4.2 Primal and dual problems

A linear programme is a constrained optimisation problem which takes a particular linear form. It can be expressed as a special case of equations (3.1):

Maximise: $\quad b_1 x_1 + b_2 x_2 + \cdots + b_n x_n$

subject to: $\quad a_{11} x_1 + a_{12} x_2 + \cdots + a_{1n} x_n \leq c_1$

$\qquad\qquad a_{21} x_1 + a_{22} x_2 + \cdots + a_{2n} x_n \leq c_2$

$$a_{k1} x_1 + a_{k2} x_2 + \cdots + a_{kn} x_n \leq c_k \qquad (4.1)$$

and

$$x_1 \cdots x_n \geq 0$$

Where $b_1, \ldots, b_n, c_1, \ldots, c_k$ and $a_{11}, \ldots, a_{kn}$ are constants. Problem (4.1) will be referred to as the *primal programme*. It is immediately clear that a great deal of paper and ink can be saved by expressing linear programmes in matrix and vector notation, which should be familiar from school mathematics. Let A represent the $k \times n$ matrix:

$$\begin{bmatrix} a_{11} & a_{12} & \cdots & a_{1n} \\ a_{21} & a_{22} & \cdots & a_{2n} \\ a_{k1} & a_{k2} & \cdots & a_{kn} \end{bmatrix}$$

(We often write $A = [a_{ij}]$.)

Let $\mathbf{x}$ denote the *column* vector

$$\begin{bmatrix} x_1 \\ \cdot \\ \cdot \\ \cdot \\ x_n \end{bmatrix}$$

and let M' denote the *transpose* of M, obtained by taking the jth row of M as the jth column of M', for $j = 1, \ldots, k$. Thus the column vector

$$\mathbf{b} = \begin{bmatrix} b_1 \\ \cdot \\ \cdot \\ \cdot \\ b_n \end{bmatrix}$$

has, as transpose, the *row* vector $\mathbf{b}' = (b_1, \ldots, b_n)$. Using matrix and vector notation the linear programme (4.1) can now be expressed:

Maximise: $\qquad\qquad \mathbf{b}'\mathbf{x}$

subject to: $\qquad\qquad A\mathbf{x} \leq \mathbf{c}$ $\hfill (4.2)$

$$\mathbf{x} \geq \mathbf{0}$$

Where $\mathbf{b}, A, \mathbf{c}$ are constants

Consider a profit-maximising chemical firm which produces three chemicals which it can sell at profits per unit of 100, 200 and

300 respectively. One unit of each chemical requires respectively 10, 15 and 45 cubic metres of storage space. Producing a unit of each chemical entails the production of 5, 20 and 10 units respectively of a pollutant. The firm has a total available storage capacity of 250 cubic metres and the government requires it to produce no more than 200 units of pollutant.

Let x, y, and z represent quantities of the three chemicals. Then the firm is attempting to:

Maximise: $100x + 200y + 300z$
$$\left.\begin{array}{ll} \text{subject to:} & \begin{array}{l} 10x + 15y + 45z \leq 250 \text{ (storage constraint)} \\ 5x + 20y + 10z \leq 200 \text{ (pollution constraint)} \\ x, y, z \geq 0 \end{array} \end{array}\right\} \quad (4.3)$$

In matrix notation this can be written:

Maximise $(100 \quad 200 \quad 300) \begin{bmatrix} x \\ y \\ z \end{bmatrix}$

subject to: $\begin{bmatrix} 10 & 15 & 45 \\ 5 & 10 & 10 \end{bmatrix} \begin{bmatrix} x \\ y \\ z \end{bmatrix} \leq \begin{bmatrix} 250 \\ 200 \end{bmatrix}$

and $\begin{bmatrix} x \\ y \\ z \end{bmatrix} \geq \begin{bmatrix} 0 \\ 0 \\ 0 \end{bmatrix}$

Definition 4.1

A vector which satisfies the inequality constraints of a linear programme is called a *feasible* vector. The set of all feasible vectors for a given programme is called the *feasible region*.

Exercise

Show that the feasible region of a linear programme is a convex set.

Definition 4.2

A feasible vector which maximises (or minimises, as appropriate) the objective function of a linear programme is called an *optimal vector* or *optimum*.

Definition 4.3

The value of the objective function of a linear programme calculated at an optimum is called the *value* of the programme.

We now define the *dual programme* of (4.2), introducing a vector (**y**) of *dual variables*. There are k dual variables, one for each constraint in the primal programme. An economic interpretation of the dual programme will be discussed later in this chapter.

Definition 4.4

Let **y** be a real k-vector then the *dual programme* of (4.2) is simply:

$$\left.\begin{array}{ll} \text{Minimise:} & \mathbf{c}'\,\mathbf{y} \\ \text{subject to:} & \mathbf{y}'A \geqslant \mathbf{b}' \\ \text{and} & \mathbf{y} \geqslant \mathbf{0} \end{array}\right\} \tag{4.4}$$

Returning to the chemical firm discussed above, the dual programme can be obtained readily from the primal programme (4.3). Take dual variables λ for the storage constraint and μ for the pollution constraint. The dual programme is:

$$\left.\begin{array}{lrcr} \text{Minimise:} & 250\lambda & + & 200\mu \\ \text{subject to:} & 10\lambda & + & 5\mu \geqslant 100 \\ & 15\lambda & + & 20\mu \geqslant 200 \\ & 45\lambda & + & 10\mu \geqslant 300 \\ & & \lambda, \mu & \geqslant 0 \end{array}\right\} \tag{4.5}$$

Note that there is a dual constraint corresponding to each primal variable. The feasible region for the programme (4.5) is shown in Fig. 4.1. Note that it has four corners or vertices.

It should be clear that taking the dual of the dual simply leads back to the primal. The reader can check this by taking the dual of (4.5) which should simply generate the primal (4.3).

4.3 Duality theorems

The reader may well have noticed a similarity between the dual

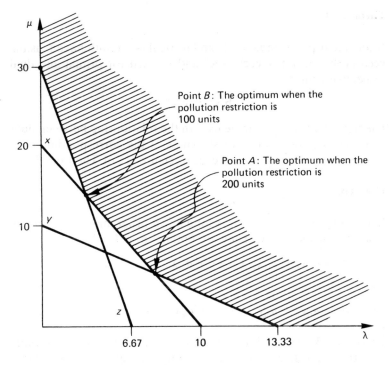

Fig. 4.1 Feasible region for the dual programme (4.5).

variables of this chapter and the multipliers of the previous one. There is indeed a similarity but we do not pursue the Kuhn–Tucker approach here. Instead we state three theorems relating primal and dual programmes. The first gives a sufficient condition for optima of primal and dual, in terms of their values.

Theorem 4.1

Let x^* and y^* be feasible vectors for the primal problem (4.2) and its dual (4.4) respectively. If:

$$b'x^* = c'y^*$$

then x^* and y^* are optima for primal and dual respectively.

The next theorem is a partial converse of this result.

Theorem 4.2

If the linear programme (4.2) and its dual (4.4) both have feasible vectors then optimal vectors x^* and y^* exist for primal and dual respectively and:

$$b'x^* = c'y^*$$

The third duality theorem deals with the relationship between dual variables and the binding or slackness of the corresponding constraints. It is strongly reminiscent of clause (c) of Theorem 3.3.

Theorem 4.3

Let x and y be feasible vectors for a linear programme (4.2) and its dual (4.4) respectively. They are optimal if and only if:

$$y_i > 0 \Rightarrow a_{i1}x_1 + a_{i2}x_2 + \cdots + a_{in}x_n = c_i \qquad (i = 1, \ldots, k)$$

and

$$x_j > 0 \Rightarrow a_{1j}y_1 + a_{2j}y_2 + \cdots + a_{kj}y_k = b_j \qquad (j = 1, \ldots, n)$$

Theorem 4.3 says that it is necessary and sufficient for an optimum that strictly positive dual variables imply corresponding constraints binding in the primal, and strictly positive primal variables imply corresponding constraints binding in the dual. Putting this condition another way, slack primal constraints imply zero dual variables and vice versa.

Let us consider how these duality ideas can be applied to the model of the chemical firm. How can we solve the dual programme (4.5)? The feasible region is shown in Fig. 4.1 and solving the programme clearly amounts to finding a point in this region which minimises the objective function:

$$\eta = 250\lambda + 200\mu \tag{4.6}$$

Consider combinations of λ and μ which give a constant value, say $\bar{\eta}$ of this function. Such combinations are given by equations of the form:

$$\bar{\eta} = 250\lambda + 200\mu$$

and are clearly represented by straight lines in Fig. 4.1 with slope

$$\frac{-250}{200} \ (= -1.25)$$

There is one such line for each value of $\bar{\eta}$, with $\bar{\eta}$ increasing as one moves in a north-easterly direction in Fig. 4.1. If we think of η as some kind of cost, we might refer to these lines as iso-cost lines. They are evidently similar to the indifference curves ('iso-utility lines') of consumer theory. Solving the programme now amounts to getting on to the lowest iso-cost line without leaving the feasible region. Typically such a situation will occur at one of the vertices of this region. However, if the iso-cost lines had a slope *exactly* equal to that of one of the edges of the feasible region that whole edge would consist of (infinitely many) optima. In general we can state:

Theorem 4.4

If a linear programme has an optimum, it will have an optimum at a vertex of its feasible region.

Returning to Fig. 4.1 the optimum clearly occurs at point A($\lambda = 8$, $\mu = 4$). This is evident from the slopes of the iso-cost lines and the edges of the feasible region. To check, however, the reader should calculate values of η for all four vertices to see that point A has the least value. Then, by Theorem 4.4, point A must be an optimum.

From this solution several important points emerge. Firstly both the dual variables are *strictly* positive so by applying Theorem 4.3 it is clear that both primal constraints must bind. Secondly, the x and y constraints in the dual both bind while the z constraint does not. Again applying Theorem 4.3 we can deduce that $z = 0$ since it is the primal variable corresponding to a slack dual constraint. This then allows us to solve the original programme very simply. We now deduce (from (4.3)):

$$\left. \begin{array}{r} 10x + 15y = 250 \\ 5x + 20y = 200 \end{array} \right\} \tag{4.7}$$

These simultaneous linear equations can readily be solved to give: $x = 16, y = 6$. So the firm's production plan is $(x, y, z) = (16, 6, 0)$.

Now suppose the pollution constraint were tightened so that only 100 units of pollutant were permitted it is clear from Fig. 4.1

that this will steepen the iso-cost lines, moving the optimum to point B ($\lambda = 4$, $\mu = 12$).

In this case the x and z constraints bind but the y constraint is slack. Hence we can write

$$\left. \begin{array}{r} 10x + 45z = 250 \\ 5x + 10z = 100 \end{array} \right\} \quad (4.8)$$

giving a production plan $(x, y, z) = (16, 0, 2)$.

Is there an economic interpretation which can be given to the dual programme? In the case of the profit maximising problem of the chemical firm the dual programme can be thought of as minimising 'shadow costs'. This means choosing positive 'shadow prices' (the dual variables) for each primal constraint so that the shadow cost of inputs is minimised subject to the constraint that profit on each output is completely accounted for by the shadow pricing of inputs. This should be clear from comparing the dual programme (4.5) with its primal (4.3). The dual variable λ is the shadow price of storage while μ is the shadow price of pollution. This similarity between dual variables and the 'multipliers' of Chapter 3 should now be clear. It should not therefore be a surprise that these dual variables can be thought of as the agent's subjective valuation of inputs. They indicate the maximum amount the agent would be willing to pay in order to have the corresponding constraint relaxed by one unit at the margin. Shadow prices have important roles in planning of various kinds, cost–benefit analysis and other branches of economics.

4.4 Another application

Consider another profit-maximising firm, this time with the capacity to produce two drugs, information on which is given in Table 4.1.

Taking x and y as the outputs of the two drugs, the primal problem is:

$$\left. \begin{array}{ll} \text{Maximise:} & 2x + y \\ \text{subject to:} & 3x + 4y \leqslant 12 \text{ (vitamin A constraint)} \\ & 10x + 4y \leqslant 20 \text{ (iron constraint)} \\ & x, y, \geqslant 0 \end{array} \right\} \quad (4.9)$$

Table 4.1

| | Inputs per unit of output | | Profit per unit of output |
	Vitamin A	*Iron*	
Drug x	3	10	2
Drug y	4	4	1
Total available inputs	12	20	

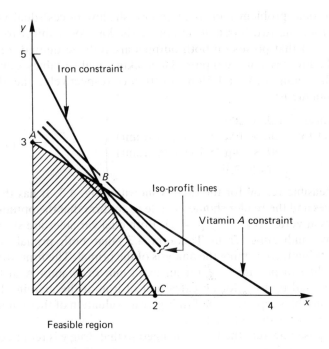

Fig. 4.2   The linear programme (4.9).

The feasible region and 'iso-profit' lines are shown in Fig. 4.2. The feasible region has three vertices A, B, C.

Clearly A = (0, 3) and C = (2, 0). Point B is found by solving the simultaneous linear equations:

$$3x + 4y = 12 \atop 10x + 4y = 20 \Bigg\}$$

(4.10)

which give

$$B = \left(\frac{8}{7}, \frac{15}{7} \right)$$

this gives values of the programme of 3, $\frac{31}{7}$, 4 at the points A, B, C respectively. Thus it is clear that point B is the optimum for this programme as is verified by examining the iso-profit lines in Fig. 4.2.

The dual problem then is to choose shadow prices (dual variables) for the two inputs to minimise shadow cost subject to the constraint that profits on both outputs are fully accounted for by the shadow costs of the inputs. Thus taking dual variables λ and μ for the vitamin A and iron constraints respectively, the dual programme is:

Minimise: $12\lambda + 20\mu$
subject to: $3\lambda + 10\mu \geq 2$ (x constraint)
                     $4\lambda + 4\mu \geq 1$ (y constraint)
                     $\lambda, \mu \geq 0$

(4.11)

The feasible region for the dual is shown in Fig. 4.3. It has three vertices and the reader should be able to confirm that the optimum occurs at vertex B ($\lambda = \frac{2}{28}$, $\mu = \frac{5}{28}$). Both dual variables are strictly positive indicating, from Theorem 4.3, that both primal constraints bind, confirming the analysis of the primal. The firm would be willing to pay up to $\frac{2}{28}$ for an extra unit of vitamin A at the margin and up to $\frac{5}{28}$ for an extra unit of iron at the margin. The dual variables represent the firm's private valuation of these inputs in terms of its own objectives.

Suppose now that the law is changed so that drug y is required to have an iron input of 6 per unit instead of 4. This slackens the y constraint in the dual, as shown in Fig. 4.4. The reader should be able to confirm that the optimum now occurs at $\lambda = 0$, $\mu = 1/5$. The shadow price of vitamin A has gone down (to zero) and the shadow price of iron has gone up. The tightening of the iron constraint has raised the firm's private valuation of iron. Note that at the new optimum the y constraint is slack and thus, by Theorem 4.4, y must now be zero. Since μ is strictly positive, the iron constraint must be binding in the primal (again appealing to

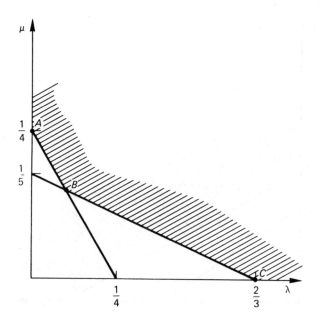

Fig. 4.3 Feasible region for the dual programme (4.11).

Theorem 4.4). Hence the reader should readily be able to show
that, with the tightened iron requirements, the firm's output will be
$x = 2, y = 0$.

4.5 Numerical methods of solution

In practice linear programmes are solved using algorithms (rou-
tines) programmed on computers. Such methods permit the solution of very large linear programmes, with thousands of variables,
within just a few seconds. The most famous of these algorithms is
called the Simplex Method, invented by Dantzig (1951). It can be
used to solve any linear programme. Consider a minimising problem in which the function to be minimised is:

$$z = c'y \tag{4.12}$$

From Theorem 4.4 we know that if this programme has an optimum then it will have an optimum at one of the vertices of its

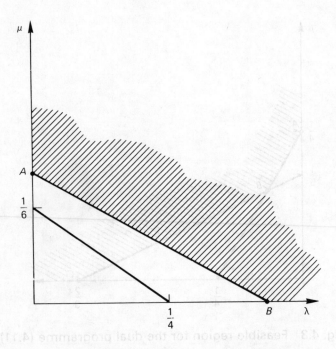

Fig. 4.4 Feasible region for the drug firm's dual
programme with a tightened iron constraint.

(convex) feasible region. Equation (4.12) is the equation of a
hyperplane orthogonal to **c** whose perpendicular distance to the
origin is proportional to z. The simplex method constructs a
sequence of such hyperplanes through vertices of the feasible
region which is such that z is reduced at each step of the sequence.
After a finite number of steps the minimum, if it exists, must be
attained. For further reading on numerical solution techniques
such as the simplex method, the reader should consult Dorfman,
Samuelson and Solow (1958).

Exercises

1 Consider a profit-maximising firm producing three goods with
  characteristics as described in the table at the top of page 61:

Good	Profit per unit	Production capacity per unit	Packaging capacity per unit
A	18	2	6
B	28	4	7
C	8	8	1

Total available production capacity = 11
Total available packaging capacity = 8

  (i) Formulate the firm's problem as a linear programme.
 (ii) Write down the dual programme and hence find the firm's chosen outputs of the three goods.
(iii) Give an economic interpretation of the dual variables. Explain how the dual variable on the production capacity constraint varies as available production capacity varies from 2 to 100.

2 A farmer has three types of cattle food available with the following properties:

Food type	Cost per kg	Units of vitamin A per kg	Units of vitamin B per kg
1	1	1/40	1/60
2	1	1/50	1/25
3	1	1/70	1/20

He wishes to mix the food-types so as to minimise cost but he must ensure that the cattle receive at least 10 units of vitamin A and 4 units of vitamin B.

  (i) Set up the farmer's problem as a linear programme and write down its dual.
 (ii) Solve the dual programme and hence find the optimal mix of food-types. State clearly any theorem you use.
(iii) What would happen to the optimal mix of food-types if a disease broke out, requiring the cattle to be fed at least 10 units of vitamin B?

3 Show that the following linear programme is feasible but has no optimum.

Maximise: $2x + 3y$
subject to: $-5x + 4y \leqslant -1$
$\qquad\qquad x - y \leqslant 2$
$\qquad\qquad x, y \geqslant 0$

4 Consider a profit-maximising firm capable of producing three goods x, y, z. A dangerous pollutant occurs as a by-product in all three cases. Information on the three goods is set out below.

	Good		
	x	y	z
Labour required per unit	5	10	20
Pollutant produced per unit	30	5	15
Profit per unit of output	20	100	50

The firm has 100 units of labour available and government restrictions require that it produce no more than 200 units of pollutant.

 (i) Set up the firm's decision problem as a linear programme.
(ii) Write down the dual programme.
(iii) Show that the firm will produce only one of the three goods.
(iv) Show that the firm would not be willing to pay a bribe to have the pollution constraint relaxed at the margin. What would it be willing to pay as a bribe if the pollution constraint were tightened to 40 units?

Further reading

Chiang (1984) reviews elementary matrix algebra and discusses linear programmes and duality. Baumol (1977) contains a slightly more elementary discussion and a chapter on applications of linear programming to the theory of production. Dorfman, Samuelson and Solow (1958) is a classic reference on linear programming. See also Gale (1960).

5 Linear algebra

5.1 Introduction

Matrix and vector notation was introduced in the last chapter in the context of linear programmes. The basic ideas of matrix (or linear) algebra should be familiar from school mathematics but they need to be developed before they can be fully exploited in economic applications.

In Chapter 4 matrices were used because they enabled relationships involving many goods to be expressed in a simple notation. Often in economics one deals with variables which are aggregates of other variables. The obvious example here is GNP, discussed in macroeconomics, and constructed by aggregating the money values of the many different goods and services which make up the final output of the economy. In textbooks, analysis is often simplified, for expositional purposes, to involve a small number of goods. Consumers are frequently supposed to spend their budgets on just two goods (apples and oranges, cakes and ale) because of the dimensional limitations of textbook diagrams. In fact, of course, there are many different goods produced in the economy by many different techniques and sold at many different prices. It is when one wants to construct models with an *arbitrary* number of goods, techniques, etc. that matrix methods prove especially useful. On the production side, for example, there are many complex flows of intermediate goods *between* industries: steel to tractors to agriculture, wheat to flour to bread to steel workers and tractor drivers etc. These flows are readily modelled using matrix methods and can be represented numerically in the familiar input/output table, itself a kind of matrix.

This chapter starts by developing the ideas of linear algebra, introducing the notions of eigenvalues and eigenvectors and stating the important Perron–Frobenius Theorem. Matrix methods are then applied to the construction of economic models of value, capital and growth.

5.2 Simultaneous linear equations

It is useful to think of a $k \times n$ matrix (that is one with k rows and n columns) as a function from $\mathbb{R}^n$ to $\mathbb{R}^k$. Let A be a $k \times n$ matrix, $\mathbf{x}$ an n-vector and $\mathbf{y}$ a k-vector: then the equation:

$$\mathbf{y} = A\mathbf{x} \tag{5.1}$$

defines such a function. Suppose y is now a given k-vector, $\mathbf{y} = \mathbf{b}$, then finding an n-vector $\mathbf{x}$ such that:

$$\mathbf{b} = A\mathbf{x} \tag{5.2}$$

is equivalent to solving the simultaneous linear equations:

$$a_{11}x_1 + a_{12}x_2 + \cdots a_{1n}x_n = b_1$$
$$a_{21}x_1 + a_{22}x_2 + \cdots a_{2n}x_n = b_2$$
$$\vdots$$
$$a_{k1}x_1 + a_{k2}x_2 + \cdots a_{kn}x_n = b_k \tag{5.3}$$

Clearly, *all* systems of simultaneous linear equations can be expressed in matrix form (equation (5.2)).

A case of particular interest to economists is that of a *square* matrix A. That is a matrix with the same number of rows as columns: an $n \times n$ matrix. In this case equation (5.2) represents a system of simultaneous linear equations in which the number of equations equals the number of variables. This equality of equations and variables (or 'unknowns') has long concerned economists, particularly general equilibrium theorists, but they have not always fully understood it.

A square matrix represents a mapping from $\mathbb{R}^n$ to itself. Consider the case $n = 2$ and the matrix:

$$A = \begin{bmatrix} 2 & 4 \\ 1 & 3 \end{bmatrix}$$

The mapping it represents can be illustrated in a diagram (Fig. 5.1)

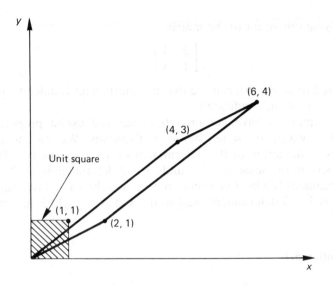

Fig. 5.1   The image of the unit square under a matrix mapping.

by considering the image of the unit square. It is mapped to the parallelogram indicated in Fig. 5.1. Careful consideration will show that this parallelogram has area equal to two units (i.e. twice the area of the unit square). It turns out that the matrix A *always* multiplies areas by two whatever the shape and size of the plane segment to which it is applied. This area scale factor is an important characteristic of the matrix: it is called the *determinant* of the matrix. For a 3 × 3 matrix, mapping $\mathbb{R}^3$ to itself, the determinant can be thought of as a volume scale factor and there are analogues for higher dimensions. The determinant of a matrix A is denoted $|A|$. There is an easy way to calculate the determinant of a 2 × 2 matrix, which we state as:

Theorem 5.1

The determinant of the 2 × 2 matrix

$$A = \begin{bmatrix} a & b \\ c & d \end{bmatrix}$$

is given by: $|A| = ad - bc$.

Applying this result to the matrix

$$\begin{bmatrix} 2 & 4 \\ 1 & 3 \end{bmatrix},$$

referred to above, we can see that its determinant is indeed equal to two, as already indicated.

Determinants have certain interesting and useful properties some of which are stated below as theorems. We start with a recursive definition of the determinant of an $n \times n$ matrix. It is recursive in the sense that it builds 3×3 determinants on 2×2 determinants (defined in Theorem 5.1), and then 4×4 determinants on 3×3 determinants and so on. Let $A = [a_{ij}]$ be an $n \times n$ matrix.

Definition 5.1

The *cofactor* A_{ij} of a_{ij} is given by multiplying $(-1)^{i+j}$ by the determinant obtained by deleting the ith row and jth column of A. (This determinant is called the *minor* of a_{ij}.)

Definition 5.2

The determinant of A is given by

$$|A| = \sum_j a_{ij} A_{ij} = \sum_i a_{ij} A_{ij}$$

Theorem 5.2

Suppose $\hat{A}$ is obtained from A by multiplying one row (or column) of A by a constant k, then

$$|\hat{A}| = k|A|$$

Theorem 5.3

Suppose $\hat{A}$ is obtained from A by adding a scalar multiple of one row (or column) of A to another row (or column). Then:

$$|\hat{A}| = |A|$$

Theorem 5.4

Suppose $\hat{A}$ is obtained from A by interchanging two rows (or columns) of A. Then:

$$|\hat{A}| = -|A|$$

Theorem 5.5

Let A and B be $n \times n$ matrices then

$$|A\,B| = |A| \times |B|$$

Calculating the determinants of large matrices is a tedious mechanical procedure best consigned to a computer, though such calculations can be carried out manually by recourse to Definition 5.2 and Theorems 5.2, 5.3 and 5.4. Instead of developing this line of argument, however, we turn back to the simultaneous linear equations summarised in equation (5.2). First we define matrix identities and inverses:

Definition 5.3

Let I be the $n \times n$ matrix with ones on the leading diagonal and zeros everywhere else.

$$I = \begin{bmatrix} 1 & 0 & \ldots & 0 \\ 0 & 1 & \ldots & 0 \\ \cdot & & & \\ \cdot & & & \\ \cdot & & & \\ 0 & & \ldots & 1 \end{bmatrix}$$

I has the property that $AI = IA = A$ for any $n \times n$ matrix A and is called the *identity matrix*.

Definition 5.4

Let A be an $n \times n$ matrix. If there exists a matrix A^{-1} such that

$$AA^{-1} = A^{-1}A = I$$

then A^{-1} is called the *inverse* of A

The reader should have little difficulty in establishing that identities and inverses are unique and, as a corollary of Theorem 5.5, that $|A^{-1}| = |A|^{-1}$.

Consider now the simultaneous equations (5.2) and suppose that $\mathbf{b} \neq \mathbf{0}$. These equations have a unique solution, found as follows:

$$\mathbf{b} = A\mathbf{x}$$
$$\Rightarrow \qquad A^{-1}\mathbf{b} = (A^{-1}A)\mathbf{x} \qquad\qquad (5.4)$$
$$\Rightarrow \qquad A^{-1}\mathbf{b} = I\mathbf{x} = \mathbf{x}$$

This is fine, provided A^{-1} exists, which is only true if $|A| \neq 0$ since, as mentioned above $|A^{-1}| = |A|^{-1}$, which exists only if $|A| \neq 0$. This in fact turns out to be a *sufficient* as well as a necessary condition for the solution of (5.2). We can now state the very important:

Theorem 5.6

Let A be an $n \times n$ matrix and $\mathbf{b}$ a non-zero n-vector. Then the simultaneous linear equations $A\mathbf{x} = \mathbf{b}$ have a unique solution if and only if $|A| \neq 0$.

Consider now the case $\mathbf{b} = \mathbf{0}$. The equations.

$$A\mathbf{x} = \mathbf{0} \qquad\qquad (5.5)$$

clearly have the trivial solution $\mathbf{x} = \mathbf{0}$. But we can also state:

Theorem 5.7

Let A be an $n \times n$ matrix. Then the simultaneous linear equations:

$$A\mathbf{x} = \mathbf{0}$$

have (non-unique) non-trivial solutions if and only if $|A| = 0$. (In fact there will be infinitely many solutions in this case.)

5.3 Eigenvalues and eigenvectors

We now turn to the first part of linear algebra which may not be familiar from school mathematics. Consider a 2×2 matrix as a mapping of the plane. In particular consider the matrix:

$$A = \begin{bmatrix} 2 & 4 \\ 1 & 3 \end{bmatrix},$$

discussed above, whose corresponding mapping is illustrated in Fig. 5.1. In general the mapping alters the direction of vectors to which it is applied. There may, however, be a vector whose direction is invariant under the mapping. Such a vector is called an *eigenvector* of the matrix A.

Definition 5.5

Let A be a square matrix. Any vector $\mathbf{x}$ with the property:

$$A\mathbf{x} = \lambda\mathbf{x}, \text{ for some scalar } \lambda,$$

is called an *eigenvector* of A. The scalar λ is called an eigenvalue of A. (The eigenvalue corresponding to the eigenvector $\mathbf{x}$.)

It is immediately obvious that eigenvectors are defined only by their direction, not their length. The reader should be able readily to confirm that if $\mathbf{x}$ is an eigenvector of A then so is $\mu\mathbf{x}$ for any scalar μ. To calculate eigenvalues and eigenvectors of a matrix it is useful to have recourse to the idea of determinants, discussed above. Rearranging Definition 5.5 we obtain

$$A\mathbf{x} = \lambda\mathbf{x}$$
$$\Leftrightarrow \qquad (A - \lambda I)\mathbf{x} = \mathbf{0}$$

By Theorem 5.7 these equations have non-trivial solutions if and only if

$$|A - \lambda I| = 0 \tag{5.6}$$

Equation (5.6) is called the *characteristic equation* of A. The values of λ which satisfy the characteristic equation are the eigenvalues of A.

Example

For the matrix
$$A = \begin{bmatrix} 2 & 4 \\ 1 & 3 \end{bmatrix}$$

discussed above the characteristic equation is

$$\begin{vmatrix} 2-\lambda & 4 \\ 1 & 3-\lambda \end{vmatrix} = 0$$

$\Rightarrow$ $\qquad (2-\lambda)(3-\lambda) - 4 = 0$

$\Rightarrow$ $\qquad \lambda^2 - 5\lambda + 2 = 0$

This equation has two real roots:

$$\lambda = \frac{5 \pm \sqrt{17}}{2}$$

If A is an $n \times n$ matrix, its characteristic equation will be a polynomial, degree n which will have n roots, some of which may be complex and some possibly repeated. The original idea of an eigenvector, one whose direction is invariant under a linear mapping, is difficult to reconcile with the possibility of complex eigenvalues. What can a complex scalar multiple of a vector possibly mean? In economic applications we are often concerned to discover if a particular matrix has one or more *real* eigenvalue. We now consider an important theorem which provides some guidance in dealing with this kind of question.

First some terminology must be cleared up. If two rows of a matrix are interchanged *and* the corresponding columns are also interchanged, the new matrix is said to be a *permut ion* of the original one. We can now state:

Definition 5.6

A square matrix A is said to be *decomposable* if a sequence of permutations of A can transform it into a matrix of the form:

$$\begin{bmatrix} A_{11} & A_{12} \\ \Phi & A_{22} \end{bmatrix}$$

where A_{11} and A_{22} are square submatrices and Φ is a block of zeros.

We can now state the important Perron–Frobenius theorem in the version relevant to indecomposable matrices. A weaker version, pertaining to decomposable matrices will be found in Pasinetti (1977).

Theorem 5.8 (Perron–Frobenius)

Let A be a non-negative square indecomposable matrix. Then:

(a) A has a real eigenvalue $\lambda^* > 0$ which is non-repeated. It is called the *dominant* eigenvalue.
(b) $\lambda^* \geq |\lambda|$ for any other eigenvalue λ
    If A is strictly positive then $\lambda^* > |\lambda|$.
(c) The eigenvector $\mathbf{x}^*$ corresponding to λ^* is strictly positive, i.e. $\mathbf{x}^* > 0$.
(d) $\mathbf{x}^*$ is the only non-negative eigenvector of A.
(e) λ^* is an increasing function of all the elements a_{ij} of the matrix A.
(f) The matrix $(\mu I - A)^{-1}$ is positive if and only if $\mu > \lambda^*$.

5.4 The open Leontief model

As remarked in the introduction to this chapter, matrix methods are particularly useful when it is important to construct disaggregated models of the economy. Consider now an economy with n industries each producing a single output. That is there is no joint production. Each industry has available to it a single technique within which there is no possibility of substitution between the inputs and which exhibits constant returns to scale. Thus, within an industry, there is no choice of technique. It is possible to relax the 'no joint production' and 'no choice of technique' assumptions but, for simplicity, we retain them.

Under these conditions a single unit of each output j requires a fixed amount of each input i. This amount is denoted a_{ij} and the matrix $A = [a_{ij}]$ is a kind of input/output matrix, called a *Leontief matrix*. Let the column vector $\mathbf{q}$ represent the gross outputs of the economy. Some of these will be used as inputs produced in one industry and used in another (i.e. intermediate goods); the rest will be 'final demand'. Let the vector of final demands be denoted $\mathbf{y}$. The reader should readily be able to verify that the vector of intermediate goods is given by $A\mathbf{q}$. so that:

$$\mathbf{y} = \mathbf{q} - A\mathbf{q} \qquad (5.7)$$

That is to say; final demand equals gross outputs minus intermediate inputs. It is easy now to solve equation (5.7) for $\mathbf{q}$ in terms of A and $\mathbf{y}$. Rearranging equation (5.7):

$$(I - A)\mathbf{q} = \mathbf{y}$$
$$=> \mathbf{q} = (I - A)^{-1} \mathbf{y} \qquad (5.8)$$

The matrix $(I - A)^{-1}$ is called the *Leontief inverse* of A. A question immediately arises from equation (5.8). How can we be sure that the vector $\mathbf{q}$ is positive? Certainly a negative gross output vector is meaningless. For $\mathbf{q}$ to be positive $(I - A)^{-1}$ must be positive (since $\mathbf{y}$ certainly is). From clause (f) of the Perron–Frobenius theorem we can see that $(I - A)^{-1}$ is positive if and only if its dominant eigenvalue λ^* is less than one. (Assuming A to be indecomposable.)

What is the economic meaning of this condition? It turns out that, provided $\lambda^* < 1$, the Leontief inverse of A can be written as follows:

$$(I - A)^{-1} = I + A + A^2 + \ldots \qquad (5.9)$$

This is analogous to the expansion (for a real number x)

$$\frac{1}{1-x} = 1 + x + x^2 + x^3 + \ldots \qquad \text{where } -1 < x < 1.$$

So equation (5.8) can be written:

$$\mathbf{q} = \mathbf{y} + A\mathbf{y} + A^2\mathbf{y} + A^3\mathbf{y} + \cdots + \cdots \qquad (5.10)$$

The gross output vector is thus broken down into final demand ($\mathbf{y}$) inputs to final demand ($A\mathbf{y}$), inputs to inputs to final demand ($A^2\mathbf{y}$) and so on *ad infinitum*. A Leontief type economy is said to be *viable* if it can produce non-negative final demands. That is to say it can produce enough output to cover its requirements for intermediate inputs. Otherwise the economy's stocks of goods would eventually be depleted and production would have to cease. Thus viability of the economy corresponds to a dominant eigenvalue less than unity. Clause (e) of the Perron–Frobenius theorem tells us that any increase in any input requirement anywhere in the economy makes viability less likely.

5.5 Neo-Ricardian models

Retaining the assumption of the 'linear technology' of the Leontief model, let us turn now to a class of model which has been involved in a measure of theoretical controversy within economics. Most economics students will have come across the notorious 'Cambridge controversies' in capital theory. (An interesting, blow by blow, account can be found in Harcourt (1972).) In simple neo-classical theory there is an aggregate production function linking output to labour and capital. In equilibrium the rate of profit is equal to the marginal product of capital and thus the functional distribution of income (its division between wages and profit) is determined. But what can this aggregate of capital possibly mean? After much argument it came to be accepted that to calculate a meaningful capital aggregate one would have to know the profit rate in advance. Thus one would be forced into arguing in a circle: knowing the profit rate to construct a capital aggregate to calculate the marginal product of capital to determine the profit rate.

The anti-neoclassical side of this argument (a group I shall call the 'neo-Ricardians') advanced an alternative approach involving a different notion of capital. It was the idea of capital as a 'revolving fund': money advanced by capitalists to get production going. Production is a process which takes time and capitalists must therefore wait until the product is sold before they can recover their capital.

To understand the mechanism of neo-Ricardian models we now construct a simple version of such a model. For a more detailed discussion the reader is referred to Broome (1983) and Mainwaring (1984). First we distinguish labour inputs from non-labour inputs. We may think of labour as the only non-produced factor of production and possibly as having some special significance in the theory of value. Steedman (1977) discusses this latter point in an interesting and controversial way. So the matrix $A = [a_{ij}]$ now represents the non-labour inputs to production. That is a_{ij} is the amount of non-labour input i used to produce a single unit of good j. The assumptions of no choice of technique and no joint production are, for the moment, retained. Let the vector $\mathbf{a} = (a_1, \ldots, a_n)$ represent the labour inputs to production. That is a_j is the amount of labour required to produce a single unit of good j. Let m represent the money wage rate which is assumed to be paid *ex post*; that is *after* production has taken place. On this assumption wages are seen not to be a part of the revolving fund of capital. This assumption has been much argued over but it does not, in fact, much affect the analysis. Let r represent the rate of profit. This is taken to mean the mark-up earned by capitalists on the capital they advance. It is crucial to neo-Ricardian analysis that this rate of profit is assumed to be equal between industries. This is a kind of equilibrium condition. If profit rates differ between industries capitalists are supposed to shift their capital from the low to the high profit industries thus bringing about the equalisation of profit rates. This interpretation highlights the neo-Ricardian treatment of (private) capital as a revolving fund rather than a stock of capital *goods* which might be specific to a particular industry. Let $\mathbf{p}$ represent a vector of prices for the n goods in the economy. By choice of units the gross outputs of each industry are normalised to unity. The reader should be able readily to confirm that the row vector of production costs is given by $\mathbf{p}A + m\mathbf{a}$, the sum of non-labour costs and wages. It is the non-labour costs that the capitalists must advance in order to get production going and on which they earn the rate of profit r. Prices must therefore be such as to provide a mark-up of r on non-labour costs of production. Thus:

$$\mathbf{p} = (1 + r)\mathbf{p}A + m\mathbf{a} \tag{5.11}$$
$$\Rightarrow \quad m\mathbf{a} = \mathbf{p}[I - (1 + r)A]$$
$$\Rightarrow \quad \mathbf{p} = m\mathbf{a}[I - (1 + r)A]^{-1} \tag{5.12}$$

Equation (5.12) links prices, the wage rate and the profit rate but none of these variables can be determined without further assumptions. Suppose therefore that workers spend all their income on an exogenously given bundle of goods $\mathbf{w}$ (a column vector). They are assumed to save nothing. Let L denote the total amount of labour employed. Then

$$L = a_1 + a_2 + \cdots + a_n \tag{5.13}$$

The whole wage bill must then exactly purchase the 'wage bundle' $\mathbf{w}$; that is

$$mL = \mathbf{p}\mathbf{w} \tag{5.14}$$

One may wish to think of $\mathbf{w}/L$ as some exogenously given subsistence wage or perhaps as the outcome of a wages struggle determined by the balance of class forces.

Substituting (5.14) in (5.12) we obtain:

$$mL = ma[I-(1 + r)A]^{-1}w$$
$$\Rightarrow \qquad L = a[I-(1 + r)A]^{-1}w \qquad (5.15)$$

With L, a, A and w given (5.15) defines a unique profit rate r. Equation (5.12) can then be used to calculate prices p. This illustrates a central feature of the neo-Ricardian approach namely that prices and the rate of profit are determined by the technical conditions of production together with exogenously given real wages.

To illustrate this neo-Ricardian type of model let us now consider a numerical example. Consider a two-sector linear economy with the following table of inputs and outputs.

Table 5.1

	Inputs		Outputs	
	Iron	*Labour*	*Iron*	*Corn*
Iron industry	1	3	3	—
Corn industry	2	7	—	10
Totals	3	10	3	10

Let p_i and p_c represent the prices of iron and corn respectively.

We suppose that workers consume x units of corn and that $0 \leqslant x \leqslant 10$, and the money wage w to be paid *ex post*. Noting now that gross outputs are not normalised to unity it is easy to write down equations corresponding to (5.11):

$$\left. \begin{array}{l} 3p_i = (1 + r)p_i + 3w \\ 10p_c = (1 + r)2p_i + 7w \end{array} \right\} \qquad (5.16)$$

With wage paid *ex post* they do not constitute part of the revolving fund of capital and therefore do not attract profits at a rate r. Since the 10 units of labour employed must be paid wages which exactly purchase x units of corn we can write

$$10w = p_c x$$
$$\Rightarrow \quad w = \frac{p_c x}{10} \qquad (5.17)$$

Substituting (5.17) into (5.16) we obtain:

$$3p_i = (1 + r)p_i + \frac{3p_c x}{10}$$

$$10p_c = (1 + r)2p_i + \frac{7p_c x}{10}$$

$$(5.18)$$

Rearranging (5.18), using matrix notation gives:

$$\begin{bmatrix} 30 - 10(1 + r) & -3x \\ -20(1 + r) & 100 - 7x \end{bmatrix} \begin{bmatrix} p_i \\ p_c \end{bmatrix} = \begin{bmatrix} 0 \\ 0 \end{bmatrix} \quad (5.19)$$

For 5.19 to have non-trivial solutions in prices p_i and p_c it must be the case (by Theorem 5.7) that:

$$\begin{vmatrix} 30 - 10(1 + r) & -3x \\ -20(1 + r) & 100 - 7x \end{vmatrix} = 0$$

$\Rightarrow \quad (30 - 10(1 + r))(100 - 7x) - 3x20(1 + r) = 0$

$\Rightarrow \quad 1 + r = \dfrac{300 - 21x}{100 - x}$

$$(5.20)$$

Equation (5.20) gives a trade-off between the profit rate, r and the 'real wage' x (see figure 5.2). The maximum possible profit rate occurs when workers consume nothing, i.e. when $x = 0$. In this case $r = 2$. If workers consume all the corn output the profit rate is zero (i.e. when $x = 10$, $r = 0$). Note that there is no surplus output of iron; the whole iron output is required in the form of intermediate inputs.

The reader should now fix a value for x between zero and 10, determine the corresponding r and then solve equations (5.19) for prices p_i and p_c. Of course there will be an infinite number of solutions indicating that only *relative* prices are determined. Prices can be normalised by arbitrarily fixing one of them at unity or, via equation (5.17), by assuming an exogenously given *money* wage rate.

We now turn to the question of economic growth in the Neo-Ricardian framework. Variables are now growing over time so we drop the normalisation of gross outputs to unity and reproduce equation (5.7) in upper-case letters making gross and net output functions of time, t.

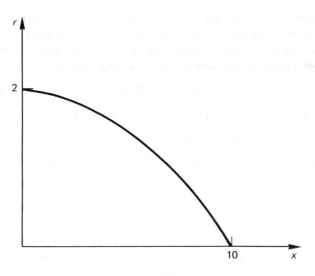

Fig. 5.2

$$\mathbf{Y}(t) = \mathbf{Q}(t) - A\mathbf{Q}(t) \qquad (5.21)$$

Labour is treated as a non-produced input growing at a constant exponential rate g:

$$L(t) = L_0(1 + g)^t \qquad (5.22)$$

We confine attention to growth paths on which labour is fully employed:

$$\mathbf{a}.\mathbf{Q}(t) = L(t) \qquad (5.23)$$

(where $\mathbf{a}.\mathbf{Q}(t)$ denotes the *scalar* product)

We suppose that the net output of the economy, $\mathbf{Y}(t)$ is divided between consumption $\mathbf{C}(t)$ and investment $\mathbf{J}(t)$, both treated as column vectors. Thus (5.2) implies

$$\mathbf{Q}(t) - A\mathbf{Q}(t) - \mathbf{J}(t) = \mathbf{C}(t) \qquad (5.24)$$

Suppose now that there is a constant per capita consumption vector, $\mathbf{c}$. This is analogous to the exogenous 'wage bundle' discussed above. Then:

$$\mathbf{c} \quad = \mathbf{C}(t)/L(t)$$
$$\Rightarrow \qquad \mathbf{C}(t) \ = \mathbf{c}L(t) = \mathbf{c}L_0(1 + g)^t \qquad (5.25)$$

The economy is growing at a rate g and constant returns to scale prevail within each technique. Inputs to production must therefore be increased at a rate g from one period to the next, a process brought about by investment. Thus we may write:

$$\mathbf{J}(t) = gA\mathbf{Q}(t) \qquad (5.26)$$

Substituting (5.25) and (5.26) in (5.24) we obtain:

$$\mathbf{Q}(t) - A\mathbf{Q}(t) - gA\mathbf{Q}(t) = \mathbf{c}L(t) \qquad (5.27)$$

and dividing through by $L(t)$ to obtain a 'per capita' version of (5.27):

$$\mathbf{q} - A\mathbf{q} - gA\mathbf{q} = \mathbf{c}$$
$$=> \qquad \mathbf{q} = [I - (1 + g)]^{-1}\mathbf{c} \qquad (5.28)$$

This bears a marked resemblance to equation (5.12). In fact, taking wages to be paid *ex post* equation (5.11) becomes

$$\mathbf{p} = (1 + r)\mathbf{p}A + m\mathbf{a} \qquad (5.29)$$

Normalising to $m = 1$ gives

$$\mathbf{p}\,[I - (1 + r)A] = \mathbf{a}$$
$$=> \mathbf{p} = \mathbf{a}[I - (1 + r)A]^{-1} \qquad (5.30)$$

There is a striking duality between (5.30) and (5.28) which becomes clearer when the model is closed. The wage rate must exactly purchase a given wage bundle $\mathbf{w}$, so with $m = 1$ we have

$$1 = \mathbf{p}\mathbf{w} \qquad (5.31)$$

Combining (5.31) and (5.30) we obtain:

$$1 = \mathbf{a}[I - (1 + r)A]^{-1}\mathbf{w} \qquad (5.32)$$

Note now that:

$$\mathbf{a}.\mathbf{q} = \tfrac{1}{L}\,(a_1Q_1 + \cdots + a_nQ_n) = \tfrac{L}{L} = 1 \qquad (5.33)$$

Hence, from (5.28):

$$1 = \mathbf{a}[I - (1 + g)A]^{-1}\mathbf{c} \qquad (5.34)$$

Note now the exact duality between (5.32) relating the profit rate r to the wage bundle $\mathbf{w}$ and (5.34) relating growth rate g to the consumption bundle $\mathbf{c}$. They are exactly the same relationship. This result is central to neo-Ricardian analysis. If we now add some savings assumptions to the model it can be closed. Suppose, for example, that only workers consume, then $\mathbf{c} = \mathbf{w}$. The profit rate r must then be equal to the exogenously given growth rate g.

Exercises

1 Let $A = \begin{bmatrix} \frac{1}{2} & \frac{1}{2} \\ \frac{1}{8} & \frac{1}{2} \end{bmatrix}$

Calculate the eigenvalues of A and hence show that it is productive.
Suppose A to be a Leontief matrix for an economy with a final demand vector of $\begin{bmatrix} 2 \\ 1 \end{bmatrix}$

Calculate the gross output of the economy.

2 Calculate the eigenvalues and eigenvectors of the matrix.

$$\begin{bmatrix} 1 & 1 & 5 \\ 4 & 1 & 3 \\ 0 & 0 & 1 \end{bmatrix}$$

3 Let A be a matrix with distinct eigenvalues and let Q be the matrix whose columns are the eigenvectors of A. Prove that $Q^{-1}AQ$ is a matrix with the eigenvalues of A along the diagonal and zeros everywhere else.

4 Consider a two-sector linear economy with joint production described below:

	Inputs			Outputs	
	Good 1	Good 2	Labour	Good 1	Good 2
Sector 1	5	0	1	6	6
Sector 2	0	2	1	9	3

Normalise to a wage rate of 1 (assumed to be paid *ex post*), which exactly purchases one unit of each good. Deduce the prices of the two goods and the rate of profit.

5 Consider a linear economy with two production processes,

each exhibiting joint production. Let inputs per unit of labour time be given by:

	Process 1	Process 2
Good 1	5	0
Good 2	0	10

and outputs per unit of labour time by:

	Process 1	Process 2
Good 1	6	3
Good 2	1	12

Workers consume a wage bundle $(3, 5)$ (i.e. 3 units of good 1 and 5 units of good 2). Let X_1 and X_2 be the amounts of labour time allocated to the two processes:

(i) Given that the economy's net output of each commodity must be at least enough to pay the given wage bundle, write down two inequalities in X_1 and X_2.

(ii) Define the *value* of the wage bundle as the minimum total labour time subject to the constraints of part (i). Solve a linear programme in X_1 and X_2 for the value of the wage bundle.

(iii) Let the value as defined above, of any wage bundle (y_1, y_2) be denoted $\lambda(y_1, y_2)$. Do you think it is always true that:

$$\lambda(y_1, y_2) = y_1.\lambda(1, 0) + y_2.\lambda(0, 1)?$$

6 Consider a three-sector linear economy as described below:

Outputs	Sector 1	Sector 2	Sector 3
Capital goods	b_1	0	0
Wage goods	0	b_2	0
Luxury goods	0	0	b_3
Inputs			
Capital goods	a_1	a_2	a_3
Labour	1	1	1

Let capital goods, wage goods and luxury goods have prices p_1, 1, p_2 respectively. Let the wage rate (w) be given exogenously and assume all capital to be circulating. Wages are paid *ex post*.

(i) Show that there exists a trade-off between the rate of profit (r) and the wage rate (w) given by:

$$(1+r) = \frac{b_1(b_2 - w)}{a_1b_2 + (a_2-a_1)w}$$

(ii) Hence show that variations in a_3 and b_3 affect p_3 but not the rate of profit.

(iii) How would you expect variations in a_1, a_2, b_1, b_2 to affect the rate of profit?

Further reading

Pasinetti (1977) discusses linear disaggregated models including the Leontief model. Steedman (1977) uses linear algebra method to develop an interesting approach to Marxian economics. Mainwaring (1984) and Broome (1983) provide useful discussions of 'neo-Ricardian' economics.

6 Differential equations

6.1 Introduction

The treatment of time is a question which cannot be avoided by economists despite some ingenious attempts to do just that. In the Arrow–Debreu world of general equilibrium there is no room for time. All deals are made at an instant and cover a complete set of contingent and futures markets. As time unfolds these predetermined deals are simply activated: no re-contracting is allowed. This treatment effectively eliminates time from the model and, in a sense, contributes to its theoretical elegance. Elegance was, however, not high in Chapter 1's list of desirable properties of models. Time is important and an important modelling technique for dealing with it is the theory of differential equations.

The last chapter discussed a particular approach to the theory of capital, distribution and growth. The time paths of variables such as output and savings were important here but substantial simplifications were brought into play to make their treatment tractable. In particular, attention was confined to balanced growth paths: that is paths along which all variables grew at the same rate. It is often interesting in economics to consider more complex dynamic behaviour, and it is then that the theory of differential equations becomes indispensable.

In fact this chapter will deal with the theory of *ordinary* differential equations. That is, equations involving *total* but not *partial* derivatives. In particular it will be concerned with derivatives with respect to time. A useful notation for these derivatives, which we will adopt throughout Chapters 6, 7 and 8, is the following:

$$\frac{\mathrm{d}x}{\mathrm{d}t} = \dot{x}, \quad \frac{\mathrm{d}^2 x}{\mathrm{d}t^2} = \ddot{x} \qquad \text{etc.}$$

for any variable x.

A very simple differential equation was introduced implicitly in Chapter 5 when it was assumed that the population was growing at an exogenous and constant rate g. We might have argued that the rate at which the population increases is likely to be (at least approximately) proportional to the current *level* of the population. The more people there are, the more breeding goes on. Such a situation could be modelled by the ordinary differential equation:

$$\dot{L} = nL \tag{6.1}$$

where L = population and $n > 0$ is a constant. A solution to equation (6.1) is a function $L(t)$ giving the level of population at each point in time. It is easy to see that:

$$L(t) = L_0 e^{nt} \tag{6.2}$$

(where L_0 = population at time zero).
is a solution of (6.1). To see this, differentiate (6.2):

$$L(t) = L_0 e^{nt}$$
$$\Rightarrow \dot{L} = nL_0 e^{nt} = nL$$

which is simply a duplicate of (6.1). Now take $t = 0$ in (6.2); $L(0) = L_0$, as required.

In this chapter consideration will be given to simultaneous systems of differential equations; that is to *dynamical systems*. These are interesting in their own right and because most differential equations involving higher derivatives can be expressed as dynamical systems involving only first derivatives. The graphical representation of solution paths of differential equations will be discussed as will the important special case of the linear dynamical system. The matrix algebra of Chapter 5 will prove useful here. A favourite technique of economists is to take a non-linear dynamical system and to linearise it around an equilibrium. This technique and its limitations, which seem to have escaped the attention of some economists, will be explained. Techniques involving differential equations will be applied to several species of economic models, including dynamic rational expectations models and models of economic growth.

6.2 Single differential equations

An ordinary differential equation is an equation involving the derivatives of one or more variables. Throughout this chapter we will think of the independent variable as time and use the $\dot{x}$, $\ddot{x}$ etc. notation mentioned above.

Definition 6.1

A differential equation is an equation of the form:

$$f(t, x, \dot{x}, \ddot{x}, \dddot{x} \ldots) = 0 \qquad (6.3)$$

The order of the highest derivative occurring in (6.3) is called the *order* of the equation. If (6.3) is a polynomial the highest degree of terms in (6.3) is called the *degree* of the equation. Thus the equation:

$$\ddot{x} + 5\dot{x}^3 + 2x + 7t + 9 = 0 \qquad (6.4)$$

is of order two and degree three.

A solution of (6.3) is simply a function $x(t)$ which satisfies (6.3). Unless otherwise stated we will take the domain of $x(t)$ to be $\mathbb{R}_+$.

Rewriting (6.1), we have the differential equation:

$$\dot{x} - nx = 0 \qquad (6.5)$$

which is of order one and degree one. To locate its solutions we may make use of simple calculus. From (6.5):

$$\dot{x} = nx$$

$$\Rightarrow \qquad \frac{\dot{x}}{x} = n \qquad (6.6)$$

To deal with equation (6.6) it is necessary to integrate it. The reader will readily recall from school mathematics that integration is the opposite of differentiation. That is to say, integrating the function $f(y)$ is finding a function $F(y)$ such that $F'(y) = f(y)$. The integral of $f(y)$ is written:

$$\int f(y)dy$$

So for example:

$$\int (3y^2 + 8y + 5)dy = y^3 + 4y^2 + 5y + k \qquad (6.7)$$

The term 'k' on the RHS of (6.7) represents an arbitrary constant. It is there because any constant, when differentiated, gives zero.
From (6.6):

$$\int \frac{\dot{x}}{x} \, dt = \int n \, dt \qquad (6.8)$$

The reader should be able easily to integrate the RHS and by use of the composite function rule of differentiation (Theorem 2.2), the LHS is readily calculated. Equation (6.8) thus gives:

$$\log x + k_1 = nt + k_2$$
$$\Rightarrow \quad \log x = nt + k \quad \text{(where } k = k_2 - k_1\text{)}$$
$$\Rightarrow \quad x = e^{nt + k} = Ae^{nt} \quad \text{(where } A = e^k\text{)} \qquad (6.9)$$

It is easy to see that solutions of this form are the only solutions. To do so, let $y(t)$ be any solution of (6.5) (i.e. suppose $\dot{y} - ny = 0$). Then

$$\frac{d}{dt}[y(t)e^{-nt}] = \dot{y}\,e^{-nt} - n\,e^{-nt}y$$
$$= (\dot{y} - ny)e^{-nt} = 0 \text{ (By (6.5))}$$

Thus

$$y(t)e^{-nt} = K \qquad \text{for some constant } K$$
$$\Rightarrow y(t) = Ke^{nt}$$

which is of the given form.

To calculate the value of A we need further information. Suppose it is known that:

$$x(0) = x_0 \qquad (6.10)$$

Then (6.9) implies:

$$x(0) = A$$
$$\Rightarrow \quad A = x_0 \quad \text{(from (6.10))}$$
$$\Rightarrow \quad x = x_0 e^{nt} \quad \text{(from (6.9))}$$

Thus there is an infinite number of solutions of (6.5), each one corresponding to a value of A. We can think of the solution of (6.5) as a family of functions parameterised by the single parameter A. This parameter is an arbitrary constant which can be determined from extra information such as equation (6.10).
In general an nth order differential equation will require

integration n times to obtain a solution and such a solution will therefore contain n arbitrary constants. In applications of the theory of differential equations the values of these arbitrary constants can be calculated from knowledge of the value of x or its derivatives at particular points in time. These values are called *boundary conditions*. Thus, in the above example, the value of A was calculated by knowing $x(0)$. Boundary conditions obtaining at time zero are called *initial conditions*. Thus the solution of an nth order differential equation can be thought of as a family of functions of time with n parameters. Given n independent boundary conditions the appropriate solution path can be picked out from this family.

We turn now to an important special case in which simple calculus methods yield relatively straightforward solutions.

Definition 6.2

If a differential equation can be written in the form:

$$x = \mathrm{f}(x).\mathrm{g}(t)$$

it is said to have *separable variables*

A differential equation with separable variables is often easily solved by separating two functions f(.) and g(.).

Example

Consider the equation

$$\dot{x} = \frac{x + 1}{t - 1}$$

with the boundary condition $x(0) = 1$.

$$\dot{x} = \frac{x + 1}{t - 1} \Rightarrow \frac{\dot{x}}{x + 1} = \frac{1}{t - 1}$$

$$\Rightarrow \int \frac{\dot{x}}{x + 1}\,\mathrm{d}t = \int \frac{1}{t - 1}\,\mathrm{d}t$$

$\Rightarrow \quad \log(x + 1) = \log(t-1) + k \qquad$ (where k is an arbitrary constant

$\Rightarrow \quad x + 1 = A(t-1) \qquad$ (where $A = e^{k}$)

$\Rightarrow \quad x = A(t-1) - 1$

Applying the boundary condition $x(0) = 1$ we have

$$1 = -A - 1 \Rightarrow A = -2$$

giving a solution:

$$x = -2(t-1) - 1$$

In cases where $\dot{x}$ depends on x alone and not independently on t, a useful technique is to construct a diagram showing $\dot{x}$ as a function of x. Such a construction is called a *phase diagram*. We now illustrate the use of differential equations and phase diagrams by considering the simple neoclassical one-sector growth model.

Assume a constant exponential rate of growth of the labour force. Thus we may rely on equations (6.1) and (6.2). Assume also a constant returns to scale neoclassical production function:

$$Y = F(K, L) \tag{6.11}$$

(where Y = output, K = capital stock, L = labour force).

Appealing to the constant returns to scale assumption equation (6.11) can be divided by L:

$$Y/L = F(K/L, 1) \tag{6.12}$$

Equation (6.12) can be rewritten:

$$y = f(k) \tag{6.13}$$

Where $y \equiv Y/L$, $k \equiv K/L$ and f is referred to as the 'intensive' form of the production function. We assume a simple proportional savings function:

$$S = s.Y \qquad (0 < s < 1) \tag{6.14}$$

(S = savings).

Depreciation is ignored and savings are assumed equal to investment, neglecting any Keynesian difficulties. Thus:

$$\dot{K} = I = S = sY \tag{6.15}$$

By definition:

$$\Rightarrow \qquad \begin{aligned} k &= K/L \\ \frac{\dot{k}}{k} &= \frac{\dot{K}}{K} - \frac{\dot{L}}{L} \end{aligned}$$

(The reader should verify this.)

$$\Rightarrow \frac{\dot{k}}{k} = \frac{sY}{K} - n \qquad \text{(from (6.1) and (6.15))} \qquad (6.16)$$

$$\Rightarrow \dot{k} = s f(k) - nk \qquad \text{(from (6.13))} \qquad (6.17)$$

Equation (6.17) is the fundamental differential equation driving the neoclassical one-sector growth model. To construct a phase diagram for this equation it is necessary to examine the RHS in more detail. On the assumption of diminishing marginal productivity of capital, the intensive production function has the shape of Fig. 6.1. From Fig. 6.1 the reader should be able to construct the phase diagram of Fig. 6.2. Note that Figs. 6.1 and 6.2 have been drawn on the assumption $f'(0) < n$ otherwise we would have $k^* = 0$.

At $k = k^*$ we have $\dot{k} = 0$. This is a *balanced growth path*, i.e. a path along which both capital and labour grow at the same rate, thereby maintaining a constant capital/labour ratio. Given the initial condition $k(0) = k_1 < k^*$ the solution path is determined. From the phase diagram it is clear that k simply rises towards k^*. Given an initial condition $k(0) = k_2 > k^*$ then the capital labour ratio falls towards k^*. These two types of time-path are shown in Fig. 6.3

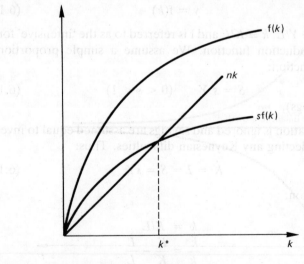

Fig. 6.1

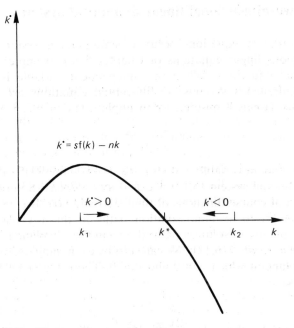

Fig. 6.2   Phase diagram for the one-sector neoclassical growth model.

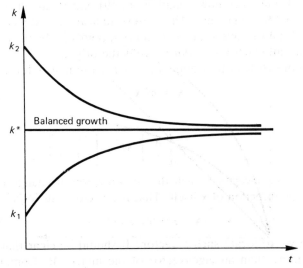

Fig. 6.3

6.3 Two-dimensional linear dynamical systems

Just as ordinary equations occur as simultaneous systems (the simultaneous linear equations of Chapter 5 for example) so do differential equations. When the independent variable is time, such simultaneous systems of differential equations are called *dynamical systems*. Consider, for example, the dynamical system:

$$\left. \begin{array}{c} \dot{x} = x - 2y \\ \dot{y} = -2x + y \end{array} \right\} \tag{6.18}$$

The independent variable, t, does not appear on the RHS of either equation so the system (6.18) is called *autonomous*. Solutions of (6.18) are of course functions of time, $x(t)$ and $y(t)$. It is interesting, however, to examine solution paths in the x–y plane. A complete picture of solution paths drawn in the x–y plane is called the *phase portrait* of (6.18). We can start by examining the paths in the x–y plane at which $\dot{x} = 0$ and $\dot{y} = 0$. These are given by the equations.

$$x - 2y = 0 \tag{6.19}$$
$$-2x + y = 0 \tag{6.20}$$

and are illustrated in Fig. 6.4.

Fig. 6.4 illustrates how equations (6.19) and (6.20) divide the plane into four segments. The arrows indicate the direction of change of the variable x and y at different points in the plane. The only point at which $\dot{x} = 0$ *and* $\dot{y} = 0$ is the origin.

Equations (6.18) can usefully be rewritten in matrix form:

$$\dot{\mathbf{x}} = M \mathbf{x} \tag{6.21}$$

where

$$\mathbf{x} = \left[\begin{array}{c} x \\ y \end{array} \right] \quad M = \left[\begin{array}{cc} 1 & -2 \\ -2 & 1 \end{array} \right]$$

Consider now a vector $\mathbf{x}$ such that its direction of change is the same as the direction of $\mathbf{x}$ itself. That is a vector $\mathbf{x}$ such that

$$\dot{\mathbf{x}} = \lambda \mathbf{x} \text{ for some scalar } \lambda \tag{6.22}$$

How are we to locate such a vector? It should be clear that it is nothing more than an eigenvector of the matrix M. Combining (6.21) and (6.22) we have:

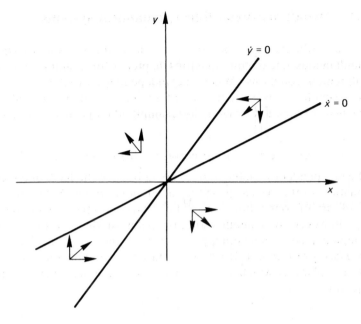

Fig. 6.4

$$Mx = \lambda x \qquad (6.23)$$

which precisely defines the eigenvectors of M (see Chapter 5). Let us first locate the eigenvalues of M. Its characteristic equation (see Chapter 5) is

$$\begin{vmatrix} 1-\lambda & -2 \\ -2 & 1-\lambda \end{vmatrix} = 0$$

$\Rightarrow$ $(1-\lambda)^2 - 4 = 0$

$\Rightarrow$ $1-\lambda = \pm 2$

$\Rightarrow$ $\lambda = -1, 3 \qquad (6.24)$

We can now locate the corresponding eigenvectors, remembering that these are defined in terms of direction only, not length. Consider first the case $\lambda = -1$.

$$Mx = -x$$

$\Rightarrow$ $\begin{bmatrix} 1 & -2 \\ -2 & 1 \end{bmatrix} \begin{bmatrix} x \\ y \end{bmatrix} = - \begin{bmatrix} x \\ y \end{bmatrix}$

$\Rightarrow$
$$\begin{cases} x - 2y = -x \\ -2x + y = -y \end{cases}$$

$\Rightarrow$
$$\begin{cases} 2x - 2y = 0 \\ -2x + 2y = 0 \end{cases}$$

$\Rightarrow \qquad \mathbf{x} = \begin{bmatrix} 1 \\ 1 \end{bmatrix}$ (or a scalar multiple thereof)

$\qquad\qquad\qquad\qquad\qquad\qquad\qquad\qquad\qquad$ (6.25)

So the eigenvalue $\lambda = -1$ has corresponding eigenvector $\begin{bmatrix} 1 \\ 1 \end{bmatrix}$

Consider now the case $\lambda = 3$. $M\mathbf{x} = \lambda\mathbf{x}$

$\Rightarrow \qquad \begin{bmatrix} 1 & -2 \\ -2 & 1 \end{bmatrix}\begin{bmatrix} x \\ y \end{bmatrix} = 3\begin{bmatrix} x \\ y \end{bmatrix}$

$\Rightarrow \qquad \begin{bmatrix} x - 2y \\ -2x + y \end{bmatrix} \begin{matrix} = 3x \\ = 3y \end{matrix}$

$\Rightarrow \qquad \begin{bmatrix} -2x - 2y \\ -2x - 2y \end{bmatrix} \begin{matrix} = 0 \\ = 0 \end{matrix}$

$\Rightarrow \qquad \mathbf{x} = \begin{bmatrix} 1 \\ -1 \end{bmatrix}$ (or a scalar multiple thereof) $\quad$ (6.26)

So the eigenvalue $\lambda = 3$ has corresponding eigenvector $\begin{bmatrix} 1 \\ -1 \end{bmatrix}$

All vectors with direction $\begin{bmatrix} 1 \\ -1 \end{bmatrix}$ also have direction of change $\begin{bmatrix} 1 \\ -1 \end{bmatrix}$, since the eigenvalue ($\lambda = 3$) corresponding to $\begin{bmatrix} 1 \\ -1 \end{bmatrix}$ is positive. On the other hand, all vectors with direction $\begin{bmatrix} 1 \\ 1 \end{bmatrix}$ have direction of change *opposite* to $\begin{bmatrix} 1 \\ 1 \end{bmatrix}$ since the corresponding eigen-value ($\lambda = -1$) is negative. This is illustrated in Fig. 6.5.

The line given by the equation $x = y$ in Fig. 6.5, is called the *stable branch* of the dynamical system (6.18). Figs. 6.4 and 6.5 are combined in Fig. 6.6 which illustrates the complete phase portrait for the dynamical system (6.18). *Only* if the initial values of x and y lie on the stable branch will this system converge (to the origin).

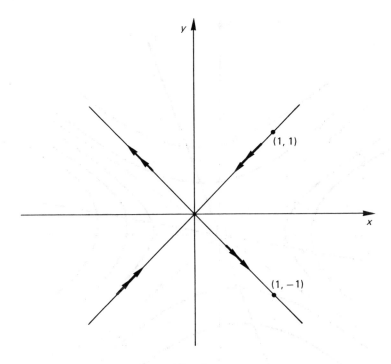

Fig. 6.5

Otherwise both x and y diverge to either $+\infty$ or $-\infty$. In economic models points at which all time derivatives ($\dot{x}$ and $\dot{y}$ in this case) are zero are often called *equilibria*. In a model with the form of (6.18) convergence to equilibrium only occurs if the initial values of the variables lie on the stable branch.

Consider now further models with the form of (6.21) with different matrices M and confine attention to the cases in which $|M| \neq 0$. In these cases (6.21) has only one equilibrium, namely the origin since

$$\dot{\mathbf{x}} = \mathbf{0}$$
$$\Rightarrow \qquad M\mathbf{x} = \mathbf{0}$$

and these equations have the unique trivial solution $\mathbf{x} = \mathbf{0}$ if and only if $|M| \neq 0$ (see Chapter 5).

In the case analysed above, the matrix M had two *real* eigenvalues of opposite sign but what happens if they have the same sign

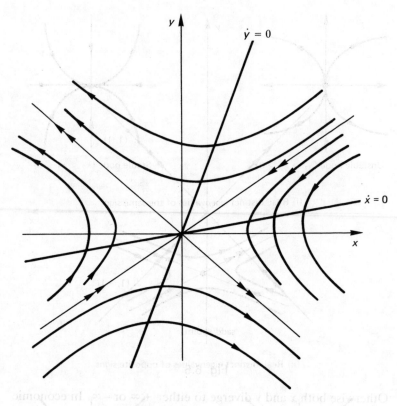

Fig. 6.6

or if they are complex? It turns out to be possible completely to classify the phase portraits of (6.21) by reference to the eigenvalues of the matrix M. A phase portrait will be called *stable* if all time-paths converge to an equilibrium (the origin in the case of the system (6.21)) and *unstable* if all paths diverge to $\pm \infty$. The various possibilities are summarised in Fig. 6.7.

There are ten essentially different phase portraits (illustrated in fig. 6.7) when the classification is carried out by the *algebraic* method of examining eigenvalues. Imagine, however, each phase portrait drawn on a thin sheet of rubber. Is it possible to stretch and compress the rubber sheet in such a way as to convert one phase portrait into another? If it is, then the two portraits are said

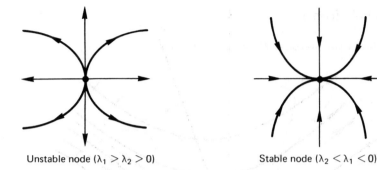

Unstable node ($\lambda_1 > \lambda_2 > 0$)   Stable node ($\lambda_2 < \lambda_1 < 0$)

(i) Real, distinct eigenvalues of the same sign

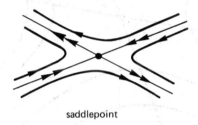

saddlepoint

(ii) Real, distinct eigenvalues of opposite signs

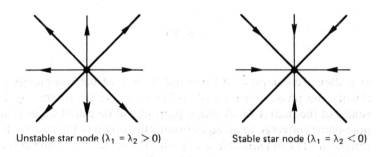

Unstable star node ($\lambda_1 = \lambda_2 > 0$)   Stable star node ($\lambda_1 = \lambda_2 < 0$)

(iii) Real, equal eigenvalues: M a diagonal matrix

Fig. 6.7   Phase portraits for the linear dynamical system.

cont. next page

Fig. 6.7 (cont).

(iv) Real, equal eigenvalues: M not a diagonal matrix

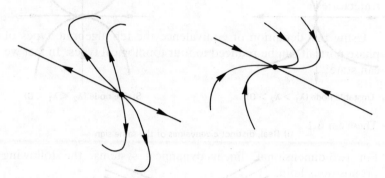

Unstable, improper node ($\lambda_1 = \lambda_2 > 0$)   Stable, improper node ($\lambda_1 = \lambda_2 < 0$)

(v) Complex eigenvalues of the form $a \pm b_i$. (Note complex roots of a quadratic equation with real coefficients can only occur in conjugate pairs.)

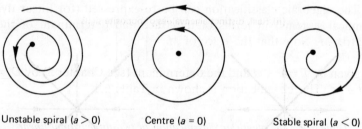

Unstable spiral ($a > 0$)   Centre ($a = 0$)   Stable spiral ($a < 0$)

to be qualitatively equivalent. Such an equivalence, which is topological rather than algebraic. is formalised in:

Definition 6.3

Two dynamical systems are said to be *qualitatively equivalent* if there exists a continuous function f with a continuous inverse (Such a function is called a *homeomorphism* and the phase portraits of qualitative equivalent dynamical systems are said to be *homeomorphic.*) such that

$$f: \mathbb{R}^2 \to \mathbb{R}^2$$

and f maps the phase portrait of one system to the phase portrait of the other in such a way as to preserve the orientation of the trajectories.

Using this definition of equivalence the ten algebraic types of phase portrait can be reduced to four topological types. In fact we can state:

Theorem 6.1

For two-dimensional, linear dynamical systems, the following propositions hold:
(a) All systems with stable phase portraits are qualitatively equivalent.
(b) All systems with unstable phase portraits are qualitatively equivalent.
(c) All systems with centres are qualitatively equivalent.
(d) All systems with saddlepoints are qualitatively equivalent.

The algebraic classification can be re-expressed (for linear dynamical systems) in terms of the trace and determinant of the matrix M. Note that the trace of $M = \begin{bmatrix} a & b \\ c & d \end{bmatrix}$ is given by $T = a + d$ and the determinant (see Chapter 5) by $D = ad - bc$. This classification is shown in Table 6.1

Table 6.1 *The algebraic classification of two-dimensional linear dynamical systems*

Conditions on trace and determinant	Type of dynamical system
$D < 0$	Saddlepoint
$D > 0,\ T > 0,\ T^2 > 4D$	Unstable node
$D > 0,\ T > 0,\ T^2 = 4D$	Unstable improper or star node
$D > 0,\ T > 0,\ T^2 < 4D$	Unstable spiral
$D > 0,\ T = 0$	Centre
$D > 0,\ T < 0,\ T^2 < 4D$	Stable spiral
$D > 0,\ T < 0,\ T^2 = 4D$	Stable improper or star node
$D > 0,\ T < 0,\ T^2 > 4D$	Stable node

6.4 Linear dynamical systems of higher dimension

The analysis of linear dynamical systems extends readily to n-dimensions. Consider then the n-dimensional dynamical system:

$$\dot{\mathbf{x}} = A\mathbf{x} \tag{6.27}$$

and take A to be non-singular (that is to have a non-zero determinant). Note that the analysis of this section applies equally to linear systems whose equilibria are not at the origin. Consider the system

$$\dot{\mathbf{y}} = A\mathbf{y} - \mathbf{b} \tag{6.28}$$

With A non-singular this has a unique equilibrium at:

$$\mathbf{y}^* = A^{-1}\mathbf{b} \tag{6.29}$$

so by a change of variables:

$$\mathbf{x} = \mathbf{y} - \mathbf{y}^* \tag{6.30}$$

equation (6.28) can be reduced, without loss of generality, to equation (6.29). Then the phase portrait of (6.27) depends on the eigenvalues of A. The characteristic equation (see Chapter 5) of A is:

$$|A - \lambda I| = 0 \tag{6.31}$$

which is a polynomial, degree n, in λ. In general it will have n roots, some of which may be complex. Suppose A has n *distinct* eigenvalues of which n_1 have positive real parts and n_2 have negative real parts.

Then $\mathbb{R}^n$ may be split into two subspaces, intersecting only at the origin, of dimension n_1 and n_2 respectively. The first subspace consists of linear combinations of the eigenvectors associated with the first n eigenvalues and is called the *unstable manifold*. The second subspace consists of linear combinations of the eigenvectors associated with the remaining n_2 eigenvectors and is called the *stable manifold*. Given n independent boundary conditions, perhaps *initial* conditions $\mathbf{x}(0) = \bar{\mathbf{x}}$, there will be a unique solution path to (6.27). If $\bar{\mathbf{x}}$ lies in the stable manifold this unique solution path converges to the equilibrium (the origin). Otherwise, it will diverge to $\pm \infty$. If $0 < n_1, n_2 < n$ the origin is called a saddlepoint. If some, or all, of the eigenvalues of A have non-zero imaginary

parts, then solution paths of (6.27) will display cyclical behaviour.
We will return to these points later in the chapter when the theory of dynamical systems is applied to the construction of dynamic rational expectations models. The conventional wisdom is that saddlepoints are of particular importance in this class of model.

6.5 Linearisation

Economic models do not in general give rise to the *linear* dynamical systems discussed in the preceding two sections. In general one is dealing with systems of the form;

$$\dot{x} = F(x) \tag{6.32}$$

where F is non-linear. Suppose that $F(0) = 0$. By the argument of Section 6.4 this assumption involves no loss of generality. Suppose $x^* \neq 0$ is an equilibrium then we may change coordinates:

$$
\begin{aligned}
&y = x - x^* \\
\Rightarrow \quad &\dot{y} = \dot{x} = F(x) = F(y + x^*) \\
&\qquad\quad = G(y)
\end{aligned}
$$

Thereby reducing the problem to the form of (6.32). We may write

$$\dot{x}_i = F^i(x_1, \ldots, x_n) \qquad (i = 1, \ldots, n) \tag{6.33}$$

Definition 6.4

Suppose each equation of the form (6.33) can be written

$$\dot{x}_i = a_{i1}x_1 + a_{i2}x_2 + \ldots + a_{in}x_n + R_i(x_1, \ldots, x_n)$$

where $a_{i1}, \ldots, a_{in}$ are constants and $R_i/r \to 0$ as $r \to 0$ where

$$r = (x_1^2 + x_2^2 + \ldots + x_n^2)^{1/2}$$

Then $\dot{x} = Ax$ is called the *linearisation* of (6.32) (where A is the matrix $[a_{ij}]$).

Linearisation is the process of taking a linear approximation to the non-linear system (6.32). An obvious way to do this in practice is to appeal to Taylor's theorem (for a statement and discussion of Taylor's theorem see Chiang (1984)), from which we can deduce

Theorem 6.2

If each function F^i in equation (6.33) is differentiable near the origin and all its partial derivatives ($F^i_j, j = 1, \ldots, n$) are continuous there, then the matrix $[a_{ij}]$ in which $a_{ij} = F^i_j(0)$ is the linearisation of (6.32).

As an application of this theorem consider the non-linear dynamical system

$$\left. \begin{array}{l} \dot{x} = y = f(x, y) \\ \dot{y} = -x + y - y^3 = g(x, y) \end{array} \right\} \qquad (6.34)$$

It clearly has an equilibrium at the origin.
Theorem 6.2 tells us that:

$$\begin{bmatrix} \dot{x} \\ \dot{y} \end{bmatrix} = \begin{bmatrix} f_x(0, 0) & f_y(0, 0) \\ g_x(0, 0) & g_y(0, 0) \end{bmatrix} \begin{bmatrix} x \\ y \end{bmatrix}$$

is a linearisation of (6.34). Calculating the partial derivatives gives:

$$\begin{bmatrix} \dot{x} \\ \dot{y} \end{bmatrix} = \begin{bmatrix} 0 & 1 \\ -1 & 1 \end{bmatrix} \begin{bmatrix} x \\ y \end{bmatrix} \qquad (6.35)$$

Thus the linearisation is:

$$\left. \begin{array}{l} \dot{x} = y \\ \dot{y} = -x + y \end{array} \right\} \qquad (6.36)$$

Comparing (6.36) and (6.34) we may write

$$\left. \begin{array}{l} \dot{x} = y \\ \dot{y} = -x + y + R(x, y) \end{array} \right\} \qquad (6.37)$$

Where $R(x, y) = -y^3$. Consider Definition 6.4 and write:

$$R/r = \frac{-y^3}{(x^2 + y^2)^{1/2}} \to 0 \text{ as } r \to 0 \qquad (r = (x^2 + y^2)^{1/2})$$

Thus (6.36) is confirmed as the linearisation of (6.34).

There is a remarkably useful theorem concerning linearisations which is frequently appealed to (usually implicitly) in the construction of economic models. This theorem tells us that, in many cases, the phase portrait of a dynamical system near a particular point is qualitatively equivalent (in the sense of Defintion 6.3) to the phase portrait of its linearisation. It is essential to note that this equivalence is local (*near* a particular point) and topological (or qualitative). In studying the global and/or quantitative behaviour of a dynamical system, its linearisation may be misleading. The theorem in question is stated below in terms of linearisation about an equilibrium, taken, without loss of generality, to be the origin, though in fact it applies to virtually all points of the phase portrait.

Theorem 6.3 (Hartman)

Let the non-linear dynamical system

$$\dot{x} = F(x) \tag{6.38}$$

have an equilibrium at $x = 0$. Then, near $x = 0$, the phase portrait of (6.38) is qualitatively equivalent (in the sense of Definition 6.3) to the phase portrait of its linearisation, provided the linearised system is not a centre.

We now illustrate the *local* nature of this equivalence by again considering the nonlinear dynamical system discussed above:

$$\left. \begin{array}{l} \dot{x} = y \\ \dot{y} = -x + y - y^3 \end{array} \right\} \tag{6.39}$$

Its phase portrait is illustrated in Fig. 6.8. The closed curve in the diagram is called a *limit cycle*. The origin itself is an unstable equilibrium. If the system starts anywhere except the origin it will tend towards regular, persistent cycles near the limit cycle. In a sense the limit cycle is a kind of equilibrium, more complex than the simple point equilibria we have so far considered. As discussed above, the linearisation of (6.39) is given by:

$$\left. \begin{array}{l} \dot{x} = y \\ \dot{y} = -x + y \end{array} \right\} \tag{6.40}$$

The reader will note that this system has trace and determinant both equal to unity (see the matrix representation of equation (6.35)). It therefore has as phase portrait an unstable spiral (see Table 6.1). Such a phase portrait is illustrated in Fig. 6.7. Note that the phase portraits of (6.39) and (6.40) are qualitatively

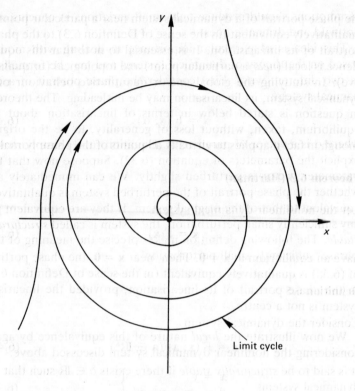

Limit cycle

Fig. 6.8

equivalent *near* the origin. Further away from the origin, however, the two systems behave very differently. The original system converges to a limit cycle which, in an economic model, might indicate regular, persistent cyclical behaviour. Its linearisation diverges to infinity, which might be taken to imply that a model from which it is derived is devoid of economic interest. Thus in modelling, linearisation is a method to be used with care.

6.6   Structural stability and robustness

In Chapter 1 an important point was made about the sensitivity of a model's conclusions to small variations in its assumptions. It was established on methodological grounds that small variations in assumptions should produce only small variations in conclusions, not wild and dramatic ones.

This idea is of particular importance in dealing with models based on the theory of dynamical systems and may be formalised in two different ways. First consider the phase portrait of a dynamical system:

$$\dot{x} = F(x; \alpha) \qquad (6.41)$$

where α is a vector of parameters. Equation (6.41) simply makes explicit the parameters of equation (6.32). Suppose now that the parameter vector is perturbed slightly. We can immediately ask whether the phase portrait of the perturbed system is qualitatively equivalent to that of the original system. If they are equivalent for any sufficiently small perturbation, the system is called *structurally stable*. The following definition makes precise the meaning of the phrase 'sufficiently small perturbation'.

Definition 6.5

Consider the dynamical system

$$\dot{x} = F(x; a) \ (a \in \mathbb{R}^k) \qquad (6.42)$$

It is said to be *structurally stable* if there exists $\delta \in \mathbb{R}$ such that all dynamical systems:

$$x = F(x; a + d) \qquad (6.43)$$

where $d_1^2 + d_2^2 + \cdots + d_n^2 < d^2$ have phase portraits which are qualitatively equivalent in the sense of Definition 6.3 to that of the original system (6.42).

The definition defines a 'sufficiently small' perturbation of the parameter vector a as one which produces a new parameter vector $a + d$ where the 'length' (in the normal Euclidean sense) of d is as small as we like.

It is possible to say something specific about the structural stability of linear dynamical systems discussed above (i.e. those of the form:

$$\dot{x} = Ax \qquad (6.44)$$

where A is an $n \times n$ matrix).

Note that the parameters of these systems are the n^2 elements of the matrix A.

Theorem 6.4

For linear dynamical systems the following topological types are structurally stable: (i) saddlepoints, (ii) all systems with stable phase portraits, and (iii) all systems with unstable phase portraits. Centres, however, are structurally unstable.

Note that Theorem 6.4 tells us that *persistent and regular* cyclical behaviour cannot occur in a structurally stable way in a linear model. Spirals either decay or explode and centres are structurally unstable. This fact has been of great importance in modelling the trade cycle.

Thus far we have been concerned with the sensitivity of entire phase portraits with respect to parameter perturbations. Economic models, however, typically include boundary conditions as well as a dynamic principle.

For an n-dimensional dynamical system n independent boundary conditions will specify which path in the phase portrait the system follows. For simplicity, confine attention to initial conditions and consider the dynamical system:

$$\left.\begin{array}{l} \dot{\mathbf{x}} = \mathbf{F}(\mathbf{x}; \mathbf{a}) \\ \mathbf{x}(0) = \bar{\mathbf{x}} \\ (\mathbf{a} \in \mathbb{R}^k, \mathbf{x} \in \mathbb{R}^n) \end{array}\right\} \tag{6.45}$$

Solutions of (6.45) may be thought of as families of functions:

$$\mathbf{x} = \mathbf{x}\,(t; \mathbf{a}_1, \ldots, \mathbf{a}_k, \bar{x}_1, \ldots, \bar{x}_n) \tag{6.46}$$

with $n + k$ parameters. Values of the parameters $\mathbf{a}_1, \ldots, \mathbf{a}_k$ and $\bar{x}_1, \ldots, \bar{x}_n$ will specify a particular solution path. We may now ask a question similar to that posed above in connection with phase portraits. Will small perturbations in the parameters lead to a qualitatively equivalent solution path? If they do, such a path is called *robust*. This time we define 'qualitatively' in a slightly different way.

Definition 6.6

Two solution paths of the form

$$x = x\,(t: a_1, \ldots, a_k, x_1, \ldots, \bar{x}_n)$$

are said to be *qualitatively equivalent* if they have the same limiting behaviour as $t \to \infty$.

The definition of 'small perturbations' is the same as above though of course it now applies to the vector $b = (a, \bar{x})$ rather than just to a. We can now state:

Definition 6.7

A solution path:

$$x = x\,(t: a_1, \ldots, a_k, \bar{x}_1, \ldots, \bar{x}_n)$$

is said to be *robust* if small perturbations in the parameters $b = (a, \bar{x})$ give rise to qualitatively equivalent solution paths.

It is relatively easy to establish the following result concerning robustness in linear dynamical systems with saddlepoint phase portraits:

Theorem 6.5

In a linear dynamical system with a saddlepoint phase portrait all divergent paths are robust but no convergent path is.

On the methodological grounds discussed in Chapter 1 we should reject any model which purports to model the dynamic behaviour of the economy in a non-robust way. Theorem 6.5 provides the basis for a powerful critique of certain macroeconomic models to which we now turn.

6.7 Rational expectations dynamics

In recent years there has been much discussion of the role of expectations in macroeconomics. In particular the idea has gained ground that, at least in some markets, expectations are formed in such a way that agents do not make systematic errors. Such expectations are said to be rational. For further reading on the rational expectations hypothesis and its role in macroeconomics the reader is referred to Begg (1982) and Carter and Maddock (1984).

For one reason or another dynamical systems of the saddlepoint variety have fascinated rational expectations theorists and we now develop a macroeconomic model which generates such a dynamical system. As with many simple rational expectations models, the expectations assumptions of this model actually boil down to perfect foresight. Nevertheless it demonstrates the application of dynamical systems theory to macroeconomics. The model draws heavily on Begg (1982), Chapter 3.

Suppose the demand for output is given by

$$Y = cY + \dot{K} + \delta K \qquad 0 < c < 1, \delta > 0 \qquad (6.47)$$

where Y = output, cY = consumption, $\dot{K}$ = net investment, K = capital stock, δK = depreciation.
Let the supply side be described by a simple production function:

$$Y = a_0 + a_1 K \qquad a_0 > 0, a_1 > 0 \qquad (6.48)$$

and the demand for real money balances by:

$$m \equiv M/p = b_1 Y - b_2 r \qquad (b_1 > 0, b_2 > 0) \qquad (6.49)$$

where m = real money balances, M = nominal money balances, p = price level, r = nominal interest rate.

We now suppose that agents possess perfect foresight concerning the price level and that the nominal interest rate is made up of the marginal product of capital plus the perfectly expected rate of inflation;

$$r = a_1 + \dot{p}/p \qquad (6.50)$$

Finally, assume that the monetary authorities expand the nominal money supply at a constant exponential rate θ:

$$\dot{M} = M\theta \qquad (6.51)$$

From the definition $m \equiv M/p$ we readily obtain:

$$\frac{\dot{m}}{m} = \frac{\dot{M}}{M} + \frac{\dot{p}}{p}$$

$$= \theta + r - a_1 \qquad \text{(from 6.51 and 6.50)} \qquad (6.52)$$

But we can solve the money market equilibrium condition for the nominal interest rate r; equation (6.49) gives:

$$r = \frac{b_1 Y - m}{b_2}$$

$$= \frac{b_1(a_0 + a_1 K) - m}{b_2} \quad \text{(from 6.48)} \quad (6.53)$$

Now (6.52) gives:

$$\dot{m} = \theta m + rm - a_1 m$$

$$= \theta m + \frac{b_1(a_0 + a_1 K)m}{b_2} - \frac{m^2}{b_2^2} - a_1 m \quad \text{(from (6.53))} \quad (6.54)$$

Rearranging terms yields;

$$\dot{m} = \left[\theta + \frac{b_1 a_0}{b_2} - a_1 \right] m + \left[\frac{b_1 a_1}{b_2} \right] Km - \frac{m^2}{b_2^2} \quad (6.55)$$

which is a differential equation linking $\dot{m}$ to m and K. What is needed now is evidently a second differential equation giving an expression for $\dot{K}$. This is readily achieved by combining (6.47) and (6.48) to give:

$$\dot{K} = a_0(1 - c) + [a_1(1 - c) - \delta]K \quad (6.56)$$

Thus (6.55) and (6.56) together constitute a dynamical system in m and K. Equation (6.55) does not contain m and can therefore be readily solved directly. The system is properly 'coupled', however, since equation (6.55) contains both m and K. Moreover it is not linear since equation (6.55) contains terms in Km and m^2. It is in fact, a quadratic dynamical system. For simplicity we express the system in the form:

$$\dot{m} = \alpha_1 m + \alpha_2 Km + \alpha_3 m^2 \quad (6.57)$$
$$\dot{K} = \beta_0 + \beta_1 K \quad (6.58)$$

where

$$\alpha_1 = \theta + \frac{b_1 a_0}{b_2} - a_1$$

$$\alpha_2 = \frac{b_1 a_1}{b_2^2}, \quad \alpha_3 = \frac{-1}{b_2^2}$$

$$\beta_0 = a_0(1 - c), \quad \beta_1 = a_1(1 - c) - \delta$$

Finding an equilibrium is relatively simple. Equation (6.57) yields

$$\dot{K} = 0 \Rightarrow K = \frac{-\beta_0}{\beta_1} \equiv K^* \qquad (6.59)$$

(K^* and m^* denote equilibrium values of K and m respectively).
Equation (6.59) gives

$$\dot{m} = 0 \Rightarrow m = -\frac{(\alpha_1 + \alpha_2 K^*)}{\alpha_3} \equiv m^* \qquad (6.60)$$

We may now apply Theorem 6.2 to obtain the linearisation of the dynamical system at the point $(m^*\ K^*)$. Taking partial derivatives of the RHS of (6.50) and (6.51)

$$\begin{bmatrix} \dot{m} \\ \dot{K} \end{bmatrix} = \begin{bmatrix} \alpha_1 + \alpha_2 K^* + 2\alpha_3 m^* & \alpha_2 m^* \\ 0 & \beta_1 \end{bmatrix} \begin{bmatrix} m \\ K \end{bmatrix} \qquad (6.61)$$

or

$$\begin{bmatrix} \dot{m} \\ \dot{K} \end{bmatrix} = A \begin{bmatrix} m \\ K \end{bmatrix} \qquad (6.62)$$

The determinant of A is simply

$$|A| = \beta_1 (\alpha_1 + \alpha_2 K^* + 2\alpha_3 m^*) \qquad (6.63)$$

which, the reader should be able to verify, is negative. From Table 6.1 the phase portrait of (6.61) is a saddlepoint and, applying Theorem 6.3, we can deduce that *near the equilibrium* $(m^*,\ K^*)$ the original system ((6.55) and (6.56)) is a saddlepoint. The phase portrait of the linearised system is depicted in Fig. 6.9.

Given initial values $(m_0,\ K_0)$ for the variables, the time-path of the economy will be determined. Note that, to ensure convergence these initial conditions must lie on the stable branch *of the original system* ((6.55) and (6.56)). This is *not* identical with the stable branch of the linearisation. Here we see a reflection of Theorem 6.5 which tells us that in a saddlepoint model, divergence is robust while convergence is not. RE theorists escape from this problem by *denying that initial conditions exist for both variables*. They would argue that the capital stock (often called a 'pre-determined' variable) does have an initial value (say K_0) but that the real money supply does not. This is because it depends on the price level which is often called a 'jump variable'. The price level is supposed always to adjust, infinitely fast if necessary, so that the system operates on its stable branch which, near the equilibrium, is well approximated by the stable branch of the linearisation. Precisely how these jumps in the price level are supposed to come

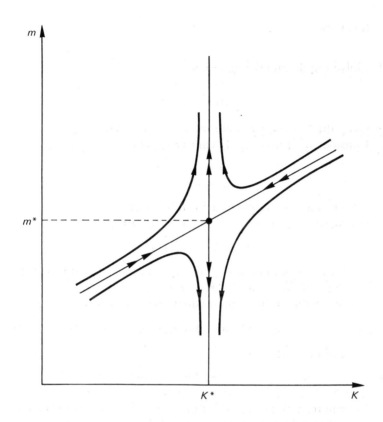

Fig. 6.9 The linearisation of the dynamical system
(6.55) and (6.56).

about is not usually spelt out. Mathematically, however, the effect
of assumptions such as these is to place restrictions on the parameters of solutions paths so as to confine solutions to those paths
lying on the stable branch. Within the restricted class of paths
convergence *is* of course robust since *all* paths in this restricted
class are convergent. This methodologically dubious procedure is
discussed in detail in George and Oxley (1985). The idea of
variables jumping without jumps in the underlying variables which
determine them is, however, potentially interesting and is developed in Chapter 8.

Exercises

1 Solve the differential equation:

$$\frac{dy}{dx} = \frac{y+1}{x-1}$$

given the boundary condition: $y = 2$ at $x = 0$.

2 Consider the following dynamical system:

$$\dot{x} = x - 3y$$
$$\dot{y} = -x + y$$

   (i) Sketch a phase portrait for this system.

   (ii) Suppose there are two initial conditions:

$$x(0) = x_0, \quad y(0) = y_0$$

   Give a condition on x_0 and y_0 necessary and sufficient to prevent divergence of $x(t)$ and $y(t)$ to $+\infty$ or $-\infty$.

3 (i) Show that a differential equation of the form:

$$\dot{x} + p(t)x = q(t) \tag{1}$$

   can be written as:

$$\frac{d}{dt}(xe^{\pi(t)}) = q(t)e^{\pi(t)}$$

   where $\pi(t) = \int_0^t p(s)ds$. (The function $e^{\pi(t)}$ is called the *integrating factor* for equation (1)).

   (ii) Use this result to solve the equations:

   (a) $\dot{x} = x - t$,

   (b) $\dot{x} = x + e^t$.

4 Kaldor's non-vintage growth model contains a 'technical progress function' relating growth rates of output per man and capital per man:

$$\frac{\dot{y}}{y} = F\left[\frac{\dot{k}}{k}\right]$$

$y = Y/L$
$k = K/L$
$Y = $ output
$K = $ capital

L = labour force

(a) Show that, where F is linear:

$$\frac{\dot{y}}{y} = a + \alpha \left[\frac{\dot{k}}{k}\right] \qquad (a > 0, 0 < \alpha < 1)$$

Y, K and L are related by the (Cobb–Douglas) production function:

$$Y = A.e^{at}.K^{\alpha}L^{1-\alpha} \qquad \text{(where } A \text{ is a constant)}.$$

(b) Suppose:

(i) $S = s.P$ S = savings, P = profits $(0 < s < 1)$

(ii) $\dfrac{\dot{K}}{Y} = \gamma + \beta \left[\dfrac{\dot{P}}{K}\right]$ $(\gamma, \beta > 0)$

(iii) $\dot{K} = S$ (investment = savings)

Derive the following differential equation for K

$$\frac{\dot{K}}{K} - \frac{s}{\beta}\frac{K}{Y} + \frac{s\gamma}{\beta} = 0$$

and sketch a diagram in (Y, K) space to illustrate the behaviour of K.

5 Consider Feldman's two-sector growth model in which investment goods are produced in sector 1 and consumption goods in sector 2. Output in each sector is proportionate to capital stock in that sector. In obvious notation:

$$I = \beta.K_1 \qquad \text{(}\beta \text{ constant)}$$
$$C = K_2 \qquad \text{(by choice of units)}$$

Suppose a proportion, θ, of total investment output is allocated to sector 1, the remainder to sector 2. $K_1(0)$, $K_2(0)$ are given.

(i) Derive time paths for I and C. Show that the proportionate growth rates of these two variables converge as $t \to \infty$ (t = time).

(ii) How would you introduce technical progress into this model?

Further reading

Arrowsmith and Place (1982) is an excellent reference on ordinary differential equations which adopts a qualitative approach and contains several applications, some to economics. A more advanced text is Hirsch and Smale (1974).

Begg (1982) and Carter and Maddock (1984) discuss rational expectations models, complete with 'jump variables'. George and Oxley (1985) discuss the notion of robustness and its relevance to rational expectations models.

7 Dynamic optimisation

7.1 Introduction

In Chapter 3 we developed the theory of optimisation, arguing that it provided the basis for a wide variety of economic models. The type of model analysed in that chapter involved agents making choices concerning the values of a variable at an *instant in time*. Many choices, however, involve the time-paths of variables from now, when the choice is made, until some time in the future. We might model firms, for example, as choosing current output to maximise current profits. Evidently, however, firms plan output levels for several time periods ahead, and are interested in future as well as current profits. Installing new machinery in period one may entail huge losses in period one but enhanced profits in the future: investment decisions must surely balance future profits against current losses. According to the life-cycle hypothesis of household saving, households are supposed to plan the future paths of their consumption and savings in the light of expected future incomes.

Whenever present and future are bound together by some objective constraint, the optimal choice of time-paths is likely to be an issue. If we catch large numbers of fish now there will be fewer left to breed and hence fewer to catch next year. What policy should governments adopt towards the regulation of fisheries? Questions such as these can be posed in terms of the optimal choice of time-paths of economic variables: that is, in terms of *dynamic optimisation*.

This chapter develops the mathematics of dynamic optimisation in a form which is of particular use in economic modelling. Throughout the chapter we will be concerned with the optimal choice of time-paths of economic variables. We confine ourselves, however, to models in which the choices themselves are made at an instant in time: we do not admit the possibility of agents revising their choices as time unfolds. To do so would take us beyond the scope of a book such as this.

Firstly in this chapter we extend the one-sector neoclassical growth model of Chapter 6 and examine the question of optimal growth. We then consider how the objective function should be specified in models involving dynamic optimisation. The mathematics of dynamic optimisation is then developed by means of a famous theorem, Pontryagin's Maximum Principle, which plays a role similar to that of the Kuhn–Tucker theorem in static optimisation. Economic applications are then discussed: to optimal growth, natural resource depletion and to rational expectations models of the type analysed in Chapter 6.

7.2 The one-sector neoclassical growth model

We now consider again the one-sector neoclassical growth model developed in Chapter 6. The central differential equation of this model (equation (6.17)) is:

$$\dot{k} = s\mathrm{f}(k) - nk \tag{7.1}$$

where $k \equiv K/L$, K = capital, L = labour, s = savings ratio, n = rate of population growth. Clearly $(1 - s)\,\mathrm{f}(k)$ is the amount of output per head ($y \equiv Y/L$) which is not saved, i.e. consumption per head ($c \equiv C/L$).

Thus we may rearrange equation (7.1) to yield:

$$\mathrm{f}(k) = c + \dot{k} + nk \tag{7.2}$$

Equation (7.2) simply tells us that output per head is either consumed, used for increasing the capital/labour ratio ('capital deepening'), or used to keep the growth of capital in line with the growth of labour ('capital widening'). Suppose now that the savings ratio can somehow be seen as a policy variable, a variable which can be set by the government. How should it be set? This is the well-known problem of optimal economic growth. If society saves a lot now it will not be able to consume much now, but it will be able to consume more in the future. The question of optimal growth clearly involves a trade-off between present and future

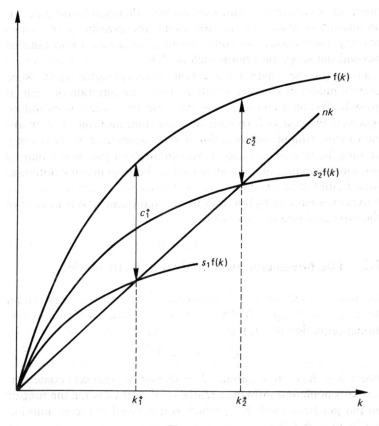

Fig. 7.1

consumption. Savings (and hence investment) provide a link between present and future of the kind discussed in the introduction,
and the optimal growth problem must clearly involve dynamic
optimisation.

To proceed with this question it is clearly necessary to specify
the objective function; the function to be maximised. The reader
will recall from Chapter 6 that the *balanced* growth paths (those
with a constant capital/labour ratio) were stable in the sense that if
displaced from such a path, the economy tends to return to it. To
locate balanced growth paths, we simply examine the RHS of
equation (7.1) and look for values of k at which $sf(k) - nk = 0$.
This is illustrated in Fig. 7.1. Evidently, for a given rate of

population growth (n), different savings ratios correspond to different balanced growth paths. The higher savings ratio, (s_2) in Fig. 7.1 corresponds to a higher capital/labour ratio (k_2^*) than that corresponding to the savings ratio s_1. The corresponding levels of consumption per head are given by c_2^* and c_1^* respectively. Note that, along a balanced growth the level of consumption per head is constant. This is clearly seen from equation (7.2), noting that, along a balanced growth path, k is constant and thus $\dot{k} = 0$. We might then simplify the optimal growth problem to the following: set a level of s (the savings ratio) so as to choose that balanced growth path which maximises the level of consumption per head in perpetuity.

Along a balanced growth path, k is constant and thus $\dot{k} = 0$, hence consumption per head is given by:

$$c = f(k) - nk \tag{7.3}$$

and is clearly maximised when:

$$\begin{aligned} f'(k) - n &= 0 \\ \Rightarrow \quad f'(k) &= n \end{aligned} \tag{7.4}$$

Equation (7.4) expresses the so-called 'Golden Rule' of accumulation: 'set the marginal product of capital* equal to the rate of population growth for maximum sustainable per capita consumption'. It is illustrated in Fig. 7.2. It should be clear on geometrical grounds that consumption per head is maximised when the tangent to the intensive production function is parallel to the nk line.

We have thus solved a very simple dynamic optimisation problem. Its form, however, is too simple for most applications. The maximand (c) is simply the level of a variable which remains constant over time. The choice variable (s) also has a constant time-path and we have confined ourselves to balanced growth paths. In the next section we begin to relax these restrictions.

---

* To see that $f'(k)$ is the marginal product of capital simply note that:

$$\begin{aligned} Y/L &= f(K/L) \\ \Rightarrow \quad Y &= Lf(K/L) \\ \Rightarrow \quad Y_K &= \frac{1}{L} \cdot L \cdot f'(K/L) = f'(k) \end{aligned}$$

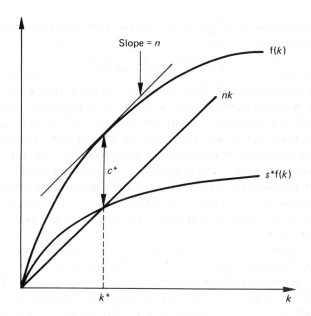

Fig. 7.2   The 'Golden Rule' of accumulation in the
neoclassical one-sector growth model.

7.3   A more general maximand

In the above treatment of neoclassical optimal growth the maximand was taken as the level of consumption per head, in perpetuity. Attention was confined to paths along which consumption
per head is constant. It may be the case, however, that agents
prefer present to future benefits of the same level. Moreover, it is
likely to be the 'utility' or 'social welfare' of consumption which is
important rather than simply the level of consumption. Suppose
then that society is made up of identical individuals each receiving
consumption c at time t and having utility function $U(c)$. On
Benthamite principles we obtain a social welfare function by
multiplying individual utility by the number of individuals: social
welfare = $LU(c)$.

The question now is how to compare present with future social
welfare. The standard approach, which we will adopt here, is to
assume that future welfare is valued less than present welfare of

the same level. In fact we will assume discounting at a constant exponential rate r. Thus:

$$V(t) = L(t)\, U(c(t))e^{-rt} \qquad (7.5)$$

where $V(t)$ = present value of social welfare at time t.

It is worth noting that this question of discounting provoked considerable argument among the pioneers of optimal growth theory. Ramsey (1928) described it as 'ethically indefensible and (arising) merely from weakness of the imagination'. He is presumably concerned here with the extent to which the present generation of decision takers should take into account the welfare of future generations. Ethically indefensible or not, discounting plays an important mathematical role, to which we return later in this chapter.

The RHS of (7.5) might follow a variety of different time-paths such as those illustrated in Fig. 7.3. The question then is how to assign an overall value to the social welfare associated with each path. First, suppose we are concerned only with events up to time T, what happens beyond that time is assumed to be of no significance *vis-à-vis* welfare. An obvious way to define the welfare associated with a particular path is simply to add together the welfare at each point in time between zero and T.

Taking time in discrete periods, this corresponds to the sum of the areas of the shaded rectangles in Fig. 7.3. Let the length of these periods tend to zero and the sum of the areas of the rectangles tends to the area under the curve. The reader will recall from school mathematics that this area is simply the integral of the function represented by the curve, between the limits zero and T. Thus, noting that $L(t) = L_0 e^{nt}$,

$$J = \int_0^T V(t)\, dt$$

$$= \int_0^T L(t) \cdot U(c(t))\, e^{-rt} dt$$

$$= \int_0^T L_0\, e^{(n-r)t} \cdot U(c(t))\, dt \qquad (7.6)$$

where J is the social welfare associated with the path of $c(t)$ between time zero and time T.

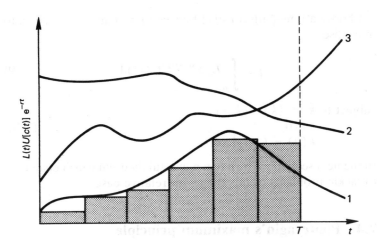

Fig. 7.3

In some applications we may wish to avoid specifying a time T (the 'time horizon') beyond which events are to be treated as insignificant *vis-à-vis* the maximand J. One way to do this would be to make T itself a choice variable and to turn the maximising decision into a 'variable end-point problem'. This approach would take us well beyond the scope of this book. As an alternative we might simply allow T to tend to infinity. Provided $V(t)$ tends to zero fast enough as $t \to \infty$ the integral $\int_0^T V(t)dt$ will converge to a finite limit as $T \to \infty$. The mathematical role of discounting is now clear. We have

$$V(t) = L(t)\, U[c(t)]\, e^{-rt} \qquad (7.7)$$

Provided the discount rate r is high enough $V(t)$ usually tends to zero fast enough for the integral $\int_0^T V(t)dt$ to converge. If it does converge to a limit we write this limit simply as:

$$J = \int_0^\infty V(t)dt \qquad (7.8)$$

Admitting an infinite horizon and allowing that $k(0) = k_0$ should be treated as an initial condition, we may then reformulate the neoclassical one-sector optimal growth problem as follows:

Choose a time-path for $c(t)$ between $t = 0$ and $t = \infty$ so as to maximise:

$$J = \int_0^\infty L_0\, e^{(n-r)t} U(c(t))\mathrm{d}t \tag{7.9}$$

subject to $\dot{k} = f(k) - nk - c$

$$\begin{aligned} k &\geq 0 \\ k(0) &= k_0 - \text{given} \end{aligned} \tag{7.10}$$

In the next section we turn to a powerful theorem which enables us to tackle problems of this type with relative ease.

7.4 Pontryagin's maximum principle

In its full generality the Pontryagin approach to dynamic optimisation is too complex to be dealt with in a book such as this. Much of it is also unnecessary for economists, having been developed with other problems in mind, such as the control of (Russian) missiles. We formulate a simplified version of the Pontryagin problem which will provide a basis for dealing with a wide variety of dynamic economic models. The interested reader will find a more detailed treatment of Pontryagin's maximum principle in Intrilligator (1971) or Pontryagin *et al.* (1962). We will be dealing with problems involving n non-negative variables which are subject to differential equation constraints. These are called *state variables* and represented by the vector $\mathbf{x}(t) \in \mathbb{R}^n$ with $\mathbf{x}(t) \geq \mathbf{0}$. Define the non-negative $n + k$ vector $\mathbf{z}$ by $\mathbf{z}(t) = [\mathbf{x}(t), \mathbf{y}(t)]$.

We express the differential equation constraints in the following form:

$$\dot{x}_i = F^i(\mathbf{x}, \mathbf{y}, t) \qquad (i = 1, \ldots, n) \tag{7.11}$$

where F is concave and differentiable.

In most applications t does not appear as an independent argument of F. In addition we may assume initial conditions for the state variables $\mathbf{x}$.

$$\mathbf{x}(0) = \bar{\mathbf{x}} \tag{7.12}$$

The maximand will take the form:

$$J = \int_0^T u(\mathbf{x}(t), \mathbf{y}(t), t)\, e^{-rt} \mathrm{d}t \qquad (7.13)$$

where T, the time horizon, may be finite or infinite and r, the discount rate, is non-negative.

Not discounting at all implies taking $r = 0$ which may mean that the integral J does not converge as $T \to \infty$. We return to this point later in the chapter. The instantaneous utility function $u(\mathbf{x}, \mathbf{y})$ is taken to be concave and differentiable.

In addition to the differential constraints set out in equation (7.11) above, we admit the possibility of instantaneous or static constraints on the vector $\mathbf{z}(t)$. We express this in the following form:

$$\mathbf{z}(t) \in Z_t \qquad \text{where } Z_t \text{ is convex} \qquad (7.14)$$

To proceed with Pontryagin's approach we now define a function called the Hamiltonian, which is analogous to Lagrangian in Kuhn–Tucker theory. To do so we introduce non-negative variables $p_i(t)$ $(i = 1, \ldots, n)$, one for each differential constraint (equation (7.11)), which are called *costate variables*. These are remarkably reminiscent of the multipliers of Kuhn–Tucker theory and, not surprisingly, turn out to have an interpretation as a kind of shadow price. The Hamiltonian is then defined by:

$$H(\mathbf{z}, \mathbf{p}, t) = u(\mathbf{z}, t) + p_1 F^1(\mathbf{z}, t) + p_2 F^2(\mathbf{z}, t) + \cdots$$
$$\cdots + p_n F^n(\mathbf{z}, t) \qquad (7.15)$$

(where $\mathbf{p}$ denotes the vector $(p_1, p_2, \ldots, p_n)$).

We can now state, in the form of two theorems, a simplified version of Pontryagin's principle.

Theorem 7.1

For the dynamic optimisation problem set out above the following are necessary conditions for an interior solution $(\mathbf{x}^* \, \mathbf{y}^*)$, i.e. one in which $\mathbf{x}^*(t) > \mathbf{0}$.

(a) $H_{x_i} + \dot{p}_i = 0$ $(i = 1, \ldots, n)$

(b) $\mathbf{y}^*$ maximises $H(\mathbf{x}^*, \mathbf{y}, \mathbf{p}, t)$

subject to $(\mathbf{x}^*, \mathbf{y}) \in Z_t$

Theorem 7.2

For the dynamic optimisation problem set out above, sufficient conditions for an interior maximum are obtained by adding to (a) and (b) of Theorem 7.1, one of the following.

(c_1) (For finite horizon problems)

$$p_1(T) x_1(T) + p_2(T) x_2(T) + \cdots + p_n(T)x_n(T) = 0$$

(c_2) (For infinite horizon problems)

$$p_1(t) x_1(t) + p_2(t) x_2(t) + \cdots + p_n(t)x_n(t) \to 0$$
as $t \to \infty$.

Note that for $\mathbf{y}^* > 0$ condition (b) reduces to:

$$H_{y_i} = 0 \qquad (j = 1, \ldots, k) \tag{7.16}$$

Conditions (c_1) and (c_2) are called *transversality conditions*.

This all seems very abstract so far, so to illustrate the use of the Pontryagin approach we now return to the neoclassical one-sector optimal growth model. The problem is that set out in equations (7.9) and (7.10). The reader should readily be able to verify that by taking k as a state variable and c as a control variable we have a problem of the type set out above (making the plausible assumption of a concave utiliy function U). We may write the maximand as:

$$J = \int_0^\infty U(c)e^{-\delta t}dt \tag{7.17}$$

normalising L_0 to unity and taking $\delta = r - n$. Taking a costate variable p for the differential constraint we may write the Hamiltonian as:

$$H = U(c)e^{-\delta t} + p[f(k) - nk - c] \tag{7.18}$$

Now define a new variable $\lambda = e^{\delta t}p$,

Then (7.18) becomes:

$$H = [U(c) + \lambda(f(k) - nk - c)]e^{-\delta t} \tag{7.19}$$

We have:

$$\lambda = e^{\delta t}p$$
$$\Rightarrow \quad p = \lambda e^{-\delta t}$$
$$\Rightarrow \quad \dot{p} = \dot{\lambda}e^{-\delta t} - \delta e^{-\delta t}\lambda$$
$$\Rightarrow \quad = (\dot{\lambda} - \delta\lambda)\,e^{-\delta t} \tag{7.20}$$

Applying necessary condition (a) from Theorem 7.1 yields:

$$H_k + \dot{p} = 0$$

Which, from (7.20), gives

$$(\delta\lambda - \dot{\lambda})e^{-\delta t} = H_k$$
$$= \lambda[f'(k) - n]\,e^{-\delta t}$$
$$\Rightarrow \quad \delta\lambda - \dot{\lambda} = \lambda\,[f'(k) - n]$$
$$\Rightarrow \quad \dot{\lambda} = \lambda\,[n + \delta - f'(k)]$$
$$\Rightarrow \quad \dot{\lambda} = \lambda\,[r - f'(k)] \tag{7.21}$$

Now apply condition (b) of Theorem 7.1. We must choose c to maximise the Hamiltonian. Suppose we are looking for an interior maximum (i.e. $c, k > 0$) then we need only differentiate the Hamiltonian with respect to c and put the partial derivative equal to zero. Differentiating (7.19) with respect to c gives:

$$[U'(c) - \lambda]e^{-\delta t} = 0$$
$$\Rightarrow \quad \lambda = U'(c) \tag{7.22}$$
$$\Rightarrow \quad p = e^{-\delta t}U'(c) \tag{7.23}$$

from the definition of p.

Thus the costate variable p is seen to be a kind of 'discounted marginal utility'. Like the multipliers of Kuhn–Tucker theory and the dual variables of linear programming, the costate variables are a kind of shadow price. They give the agent's subjective valuation of the state variable to which they correspond: in this case p is a shadow price of capital, k.

Condition (c_2) of Theorem 7.2 (the transversality condition) is easy to write down for this particular problem. It is simply:

$$\lambda e^{-\delta t}k \to 0 \text{ as } t \to \infty \tag{7.24}$$

Note that equation (7.22) can be rearranged to give:

$$c = g(\lambda) \tag{7.25}$$

where $g(.) = [U'(.)]^{-1}$ (the function $U'(.)$ has an inverse because U is concave: the reader should verify this).

Now combine (7.25) with the differential equation of (7.10); this gives:

$$\dot{k} = f(k) - nk - g(\lambda) \tag{7.26}$$

Together with (7.21) this gives a two-dimensional non-linear dynamical system in k and λ. It has only one initial condition, $k(0) = k_0$, which would seem to suggest a problem in determining the solution. It turns out, however, that the transversality condition (7.24) furnishes a *terminal* condition for the problem, thus providing two boundary conditions altogether, enough to determine the solution.

The dynamical system (7.21) and (7.26) is susceptible to the method of linearisation described in Chapter 6. The reader may wish to pursue this course which will lead him or her to discover that the system is a saddlepoint. Examining (7.21) shows that $\dot{\lambda} = 0$ defines a unique value, k^*, for the capital labour ratio. Putting $\dot{k} = 0$ gives:

$$f(k) - nk - g(\lambda) = 0 \tag{7.27}$$

from (7.26). The reader should readily be able to verify that this defines a U-shaped relationship between k and λ. This is illustrated in Fig. 7.4. The long-run equilibrium is at (k^*, λ^*). Along the stable branch $k \rightarrow k^*$ and $\lambda \rightarrow \lambda^*$ as $t \rightarrow \infty$: it therefore satisfies the transversality condition (7.24) since $\delta = r - n > 0$. The stable branch is therefore a solution, by Theorems 7.1 and 7.2. The initial condition $k = k_0$ picks out a point on the stable branch. Note that this requires an initial value λ_0 of λ and hence an initial value c_0 of c, from (7.22). To follow the stable branch the initial value of c must be selected appropriately. It is rather like the jump variable mentioned in the last chapter. Suppose we imposed an initial value $c = c_1 \neq c_0$, corresponding to $\lambda = \lambda_1$, then the system would follow a very different path, as indicated in Fig. 7.4. Note that from (7.22) c is maximised where λ is minimised. This occurs at k_g (in Fig. 7.4) the 'Golden Rule' capital/labour ratio.

7.5 An example from the economics of resource depletion

Some natural resources, such as coal or oil are non-renewable; once used up they cannot be replenished. Others, like fish or trees

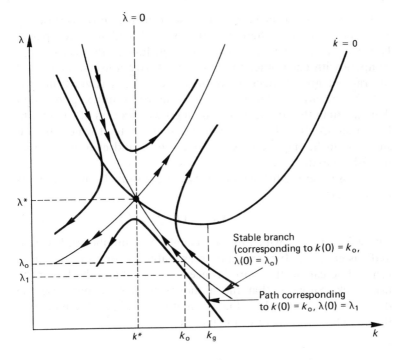

Fig. 7.4

renew themselves if left alone. In the case of fish there is a
relationship between the rate at which fish are caught this year and
the number available next year. The more fish are caught, the
fewer there are to breed and the smaller is the fish stock in the
future. Much work has been done on the economics of fisheries,
some of which is referred to in the further reading section at the
end of this chapter. A recurrent question is: would competition in
the fishing industry lead to 'overfishing'? Much analysis has been
undertaken as to how fisheries should be regulated and we analyse
here a simple model of fisheries regulation by means of licences.

First we model the biology of fish reproduction. Suppose that
the fish in question, if left to itself, multiplies at a rate given by:

$$\dot{X} = aX(\tilde{X} - X) \tag{7.28}$$

where $X =$ fish stock, a, $\tilde{X}$ are positive constant. Fig. 7.5 is a phase
diagram of (7.28).

As the fish stock increases, its rate of growth also increases at first: the more fish there are the more breeding takes place. However, as the fish stock increases still further the fish start to compete with each other for food etc. Above a fish stock of $X/2$ the rate of growth declines until, at $X = \widetilde{X}$, it is zero and for $X > \widetilde{X}$, negative. This is a slightly more complex population dynamic than the simple exponential growth process of Chapter 6. Note that $a\widetilde{X}^2/4$ is the maximum *sustainable* rate at which the fish stock could be depleted. Any faster rate would eventually drive the fish to extinction.

Suppose that the fishing authority issues fishing licences and it is known that:

$$Y = f(N, X) \qquad (f_N, f_X > 0) \qquad (7.29)$$

where Y = rate at which fish are caught N = number of licences, and f is concave. It is evidently reasonable to suppose that more fish will be caught the more licences are issued and the larger the fish stock. Suppose that the authority wishes to maximise the discounted present value of fish caught now and into the indefinite future. That is, it wishes to maximise:

$$\int_0^\infty pY\mathrm{e}^{-rt}\mathrm{d}t \qquad (7.30)$$

where p = price of fish (taken as exogenous) and r = discount rate. We take $p, r > 0$. The discount rate might be somehow related to interest rates prevailing in the economy.

We may now set up the fishing authority's problem in Pontryagin form. Choose a time-path for the control variable, N, to maximise:

$$\int_0^\infty pY\mathrm{e}^{-rt}\mathrm{d}t$$

subject to:

$$\dot{X} = aX(\widetilde{X} - X) - Y \qquad (7.31)$$
$$Y = f(N, X) \qquad (7.32)$$

taking X to be the state variable, with costate variable λ.

The Hamiltonian for this problem is simply:

$$H = pYe^{-rt} + \lambda[aX(\widetilde{X} - X) - f(N, X)] \qquad (7.33)$$

(combining (7.31) and (7.32)).

Condition (a) (Theorem (7.1) then yields

$$-\dot{\lambda} = H_x = pf_x e^{-rt} + \lambda(a\widetilde{X} - 2aX - f_x) \qquad (7.34)$$

Assuming an interior maximum ($N > 0$), condition (b) (Theorem 7.2) gives:

$$0 = H_N = pf_N e^{-rt} - \lambda f_N \qquad (7.35)$$

$$\Rightarrow \qquad \lambda = pe^{-rt} \qquad (7.36)$$

Substituting (7.37) in (7.35) gives:

$$\dot{\lambda} = \lambda(2aX - a\widetilde{X}) \qquad (7.37)$$

But (7.37) gives

$$\dot{\lambda} = -rpe^{-rt} = -r\lambda \qquad (7.38)$$

hence, combining (7.37) and (7.38):

$$-r\lambda = \lambda(2aX - a\widetilde{X}) \qquad (7.39)$$

$$\Rightarrow \qquad 2aX - a\widetilde{X} = -r$$

$$\Rightarrow \qquad X = (a\widetilde{X} - r)/2a = \frac{1}{2}\left(\widetilde{X} - \frac{r}{a}\right) \qquad (7.40)$$

Thus along an optimal path the fish stock would be constant at:

$$X^* = \frac{1}{2}\left(\widetilde{X} - \frac{r}{a}\right) \qquad (7.41)$$

Note that this is independent of the price of fish but dependent on the discount rate. It corresponds to a lower fish stock than that giving the maximum sustainable catch ($X = \widetilde{X}/2$). As $r \to 0$, however, $X^* \to \widetilde{X}/2$.

The optimal number of licences can now be obtained by solving:

$$aX^*(\widetilde{X} - X^*) = f(N, X^*) \qquad (7.42)$$

for N. Note, however, that the result of equation (7.41) is independent of the precise form of the function f. If this function is not known to the authority it may adopt the simple trial and error policy (illustrated in Fig. 7.5) of issuing more licences if $X > X^*$ and fewer if $X < X^*$.

For completeness we note that the transversality condition for this problem is simply:

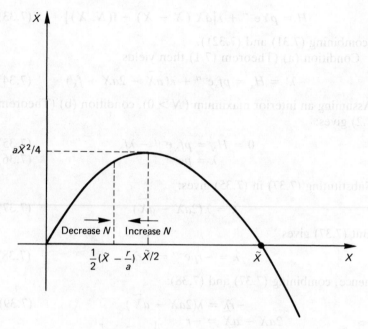

Fig. 7.5

$$\lambda X \to 0 \text{ as } t \to \infty \tag{7.43}$$

This is clearly satisfied along the path $X = X^*$ since

$$\lambda X = p\,\mathrm{e}^{-rt}X^* \tag{7.44}$$

from equation (7.36) and $p\,\mathrm{e}^{-rt}X^* \to 0$ as $t \to \infty$ since $r > 0$.

7.6 Rational expectations dynamics revisited

In Chapter 6 we noted that saddlepoint dynamical systems have come to be seen as central to rational expectations dynamics. This, it was noted, seems rather strange since convergence to equilibrium is not a robust property of saddlepoint systems. Rational expectations theorists have, on occasions, sought to escape from this difficulty by asserting that some kind of maximising behaviour will ensure that the stable branch is selected. Suppose some agent is maximising:

$$\int_0^\infty u(c, m)\, e^{-\delta t} \mathrm{d}t \qquad (7.45)$$

where c = consumption, m = money balances and $\delta = 0$ is the discount rate. Under some circumstances it is possible to show (a) that the transversality condition is a necessary condition for this maximisation and (b) only the stable branch satisfies this condition. On this basis, only the stable branch can be considered a solution path.

Buiter and Miller (1981), for example, explain that:

> The assumption of . . . the transversality condition that rational agents will not choose an unstable solution [i.e. a divergent path] mean(s) that the jump variable will always assume the value required to put the system on the unique convergent solution trajectory.

There are several points to note about this approach. First the transversality condition is not always *necessary* for an optimum. Second in *finite* horizon problems the transversality condition may be satisfied on divergent paths but *not* on the stable branch. Thirdly, and most importantly, the assumption of maximising behaviour of the kind specified by (7.45) is much stronger than the rational expectations hypothesis. It may be reasonable, as a working hypothesis, to suppose that agents do not make systematic errors in their expectations of the price level. It is quite another matter to suppose that they all maximise infinite horizon utility functions of the requisite form. An important aspect of modelling is that models should be designed to exhibit the implications of the hypotheses one is interested in. It is essential that these are not swamped by additional assumptions unrelated to those hypotheses.

7.7 The overtaking criterion

The analysis thus far has been concerned with maximands with positive discount rates. This helps to ensure that the utility integral converges as the time horizon tends to infinity. Most of the above analysis can be carried over to cases in which this integral does not converge, provided we redefine 'optimum' appropriately. Consider then the slightly more general maximand:

$$\int_0^T v(\mathbf{z}, t)\,dt \tag{7.46}$$

which need not necessarily entail discounting. Suppose we have two time-paths for $\mathbf{z}$, call them $\mathbf{z}_1$ and $\mathbf{z}_2$. How are we to compare them without arbitrarily fixing a value for the time horizon, T? We do this by means of the overtaking criteria, formalised in:

Definition 7.1

A time-path $\mathbf{z}_1(t)$ said to *overtake* another time-path $\mathbf{z}_2(t)$ if there exists T_0 such that

$$T > T_0 \Rightarrow \int_0^T v(\mathbf{z}_1(t), t)\,dt \geq \int_0^T v(\mathbf{z}_2(t), t)\,dt \tag{7.47}$$

This is illustrated in Fig. 7.6: $\mathbf{z}_1$ has overtaken $\mathbf{z}_2$ by time $T_1 > T_0$, but not by time $T_2 < T_0$.

We can now provide a new definition of an optimum time-path:

Definition 7.2

An *optimum time-path* is a time-path satisfying all constraints which overtakes any other time-path satisfying all constraints.

On this definition of optimum Theorems 7.1 and 7.2, and the analysis based on them can be retained.

Exercises

1 Timber is a natural resource which, with no felling, naturally expands at a rate given by

$$\dot{Q} = A \log BQ$$
Q_0 – given
(Q = stock of timber (tons), A, B positive constants)

The Forestry Commission can choose the rate F (tons per

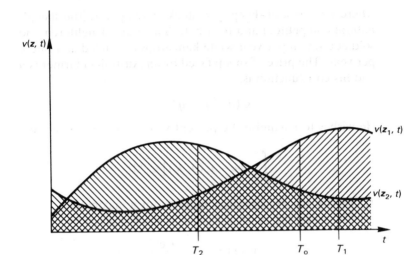

$v(z, t)$

$v(z_1, t)$

$v(z_2, t)$

t

T_2 T_0 T_1

Fig. 7.6

week), at which felling takes place. It can sell its output at a given price p and faces a cost function

$$C(F) = F^2$$

It seeks to maximise:

$$\int_0^\infty [pF - C(F)]e^{-rt}\,dt \qquad (r > 0)$$

(i) Set up this problem in Hamiltonian form and derive the Pontryagin conditions for an optimum.

(ii) Hence show that F and Q are related by the differential equation

$$\dot{F} = \frac{-1}{2}\left(r - \frac{A}{Q}\right)(p - 2F)$$

2 Australian sheep, when left to themselves, reproduce at a rate given by

$$\dot{x} = \alpha x - \beta y^2$$

where x = stock of sheep, y = stock of kangaroos (the sheep's natural competitor) and α, $\beta > 0$. Sheep are slaughtered and sold at a rate q per year while kangaroos are culled at a rate k per year. The price of sheep faced by an Australian farmer is p and his cost function is:

$$C(q, k) = q^3 + k$$

He wishes to maximise the present value of his profit stream:

$$\int_0^\infty [pq - C(q, k)]\, e^{-rt} dt$$

(i) Derive the Pontryagin conditions for a maximum
(ii) Show that the optimal kangaroo stock is given by:

$$y^*(t) = \frac{r\, e^{\alpha t}}{2(p - 3q^2(0))\beta}$$

3 It is desired to maximise the integral:

$$\int_0^\infty U(L, P) e^{-rt} dt$$

Where P is a stock of pollution and L is the (flow of) labour used for pollution removal. The stock of pollution decays naturally at a constant (exponential) rate a, and one unit of labour can remove b units of pollution under constant returns. The initial stock of pollution, P_0 is given.

(i) Explain why P is subject to the differential constraint:

$$\dot{P} = -(aP + bL)$$

(ii) Write down sufficient conditions for an optimum depletion path.
(iii) Taking $U(L, P) = -e^L - P$, show that, provided $b - 2a < 0$, r can be chosen so that it is optimal not to use any labour for pollution removal.

4 A primitive tribe gathers one unit of berries every year. They can consume berries or store them without cost or deterioration. Ancient tribal custom enjoins them to maximise:

$$\int_0^\infty e^{-rt} \log C \, dt$$

where C = consumption, $r > 0$

(i) Explain why the tribe's choices are subject to the constraint:

$$\dot{W} = 1 - C$$

where W = stock of berries

(ii) Write down sufficient conditions for an optimum.

(iii) Taking $W_0 = 0$, show that, along an optimal path,

$$rW = (C - \log C) - (C_0 - \log C_0)$$

(iv) Would this model be of any use in analysing household consumption behaviour?

5 There exists a stock R_0 of a non-renewable resource which can be depleted costlessly and consumed directly. The stock R of the resource is therefore subject to the differential constraint:

$$C + \dot{R} = 0 \, (R \geqslant 0, R_0 \text{ given})$$

C being consumption. It is desired to choose an optimal depletion policy which maximises the integral:

$$\int_0^\infty e^{-rt} u(C) \, dt \qquad (r > 0, u \text{ concave})$$

(i) Write down sufficient conditions for an optimum.

(ii) Show that an optimal policy must satisfy

$$C'(R) = \frac{-ru'(C)}{u''(C) \cdot C}$$

and discuss the form of the optimal policy. (*Without* specifying a particular function u.)

6 There exists at time zero a stock S_0 of an exhaustible resource. Let $S(t)$ be the stock of the resource and $R(t)$ its rate of depletion at time t, hence:

$$R = -\dot{S}$$

It is desired to choose a depletion path to maximise:

$$\int_0^\infty U(R)e^{-\alpha t}\,dt$$

where, $U(R) = R^{1-\varepsilon}/1 - \varepsilon$
α and ε being positive constants.
  (i) Set up the problem in Hamiltonian form and derive Pontryagin's conditions for an optimum.
  (ii) Hence, or otherwise, deduce that the optimum depletion path is given by

$$R(t) = \frac{\alpha S_0}{\varepsilon}\, e^{\frac{-\alpha_t}{\varepsilon}}$$

  (iii) What happens if $\alpha = 0$?

Further reading

Ramsey (1928) and Pontryagin *et al.* (1962) are classic references on intertemporal optimisation. Intrilligator (1971) is a useful textbook reference. See also Dorfman (1969).

Phelps (1961) discusses optimal growth theory while Petersen and Fisher (1977) survey the economics of resource depletion. Chow (1973) applies intertemporal optimisation methods to the coordination of economic policy.

8 Discontinuities and catastrophes

8.1 Introduction

In Chapters 6 and 7 we discussed the jump variable of rational expectations theory and saw that they had a crucial role in rational expectations dynamics. It was also evident that the behaviour of these jump variables has very little theoretical underpinning. They are essentially *ad hoc* constructions necessary for modelling reasons. Observable economic variables do jump however; exchange rates furnish perhaps the most obvious example. In this chapter we examine a type of model which can be used to explain such jumps in a coherent way.

Standard approaches to this kind of problem involve explaining sudden changes in a variable by postulating sudden changes in the underlying variables which determine it. Thus a sudden increase in the price of tomatoes might be explained by a sudden shift in demand or supply curves of tomatoes. This kind of explanation is consistent with the views that scientific 'cause and effect' relationships should be continuous.

Another approach is to re-examine the ubiquitous economic notion of equilibrium. The reader will be familiar with different notions of equilibrium from several different branches of economics including supply and demand analysis, macroeconomics and growth theory. In economic models the characterisation of equilibria is often of considerable importance. Having established the existence of an equilibrium it is standard practice to then examine its stability. This question was discussed in Chapter 6 in connection, for example, with growth models. Stability analysis asks the question: 'if a system is displaced from an equilibrium, are there forces at work tending to return it towards that equilibrium?' The related question of structural stability was also discussed in Chapter 6. Here one is concerned to discover whether or not small perturbations in a system's parameters lead to a qualitatively different system. This latter approach provides a clue to a new explanation of jumps. We may think of systems as being qualitatively different if they have different numbers of equilibria and consider how small parameter perturbations might cause equilibria to vanish and reappear. This is the approach of *catastrophe theory*, which explains jumps by postulating systems in which equilibria can vanish. Such a system can move rapidly from the vanishing equilibrium to another (stable) equilibrium: such rapid moments being termed 'catastrophic jumps'.

8.2 A state-preference model with non-convexities

In this section we turn back to the familiar maximising type of model discussed at length in earlier chapters. It will provide a context in which the application of catastrophe theory can be discussed.

In standard consumer theory with which the reader will be familiar indifference curves are almost always supposed to be convex to the origin. In many textbooks no justification is given for this assumption, while in others it is argued that it corresponds to assuming a consumer preference for variety over uniformity. In this section we develop a simple utility-maximising model in which indifference curves are convex in some places and concave in others. It is, in fact, an *expected* utility maximising model, in which convexity of indifference curves corresponds to risk-aversion and concavity to risk-preference. In a well-known paper Friedman and Savage (1948) pointed out that the same individual who buys insurance might also participate in gambling. This was explained by postulating risk-preference at some points of the preference field and risk aversion at others.

The agent we consider is a foreign currency speculator facing a choice between holding dollars and holding sterling. We adopt a 'state preference' approach and, for simplicity, suppose there are just two states of the world: an upward movement of the dollar (state a) and a downward movement (state b). Let r denote the present exchange rate ($£/\$$), r_a the exchange in state a and r_b the exchange rate in state b. We have therefore $r_a > r > r_b$. The exchange rate may be thought of either as floating or as fixed but subject to devaluation or revaluation.

Suppose the speculator has a budget of £L and selects a portfolio of £P and $$D$. His budget constraint is then:

$$L = P + rD \qquad (8.1)$$

and the value of his portfolio in the two states of the world (L_a and L_b) is given by:

$$L_a = P + r_a D \qquad (8.2)$$
$$L_b = P + r_b D \qquad (8.3)$$

From this his demand for dollars is easily expressed as

$$D = \frac{L_a - L}{r_a - r} \qquad (8.4)$$

The essence of the state-preference approach is that the speculator can allocate his portfolio between pounds and dollars and in so doing, he chooses between points in $L_a - L_b$ space. For example by holding the entire portfolio as pounds, the speculator faces *no* exchange risk and has thus chosen a point where $L_a = L_b$. These situations are indicated by the 45° 'certainty line' in Fig. 8.1. The reader should be able to verify that the speculator faces a budget line as indicated in Fig. 8.1. We will assume that borrowing and short-selling are possible but that it is not possible to choose contracts which would make the value of the portfolio negative in either state of the world. That is, we assume L_a, L_b, ≥ 0. It is easy to show that the speculator's budget constraint has slope:

$$R = \frac{r - r_b}{r_a - r} \qquad (8.5)$$

Interpreting r_a and r_b as the speculator's expectations we may regard R as a measure of his 'pessimism' concerning the dollar.

We suppose that the speculator has an *expected utility function S* defined over $L_a - L_b$ space:

$$S = \Pi_a U(L_a) + \Pi_b U(L_b) \qquad (8.6)$$

where Π_a and Π_b are the subjective probabilities of the two states of the world (so that $\Pi_a + \Pi_b = 1$). The reader should readily be able to verify that convexity of the indifference curves of this utility function corresponds to risk-aversion while concavity corresponds

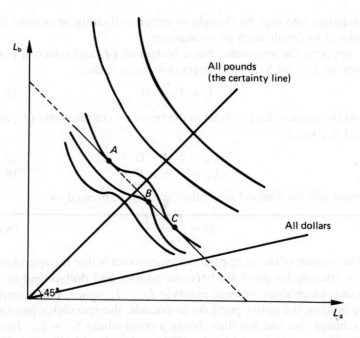

Fig. 8.1

to risk-preference. We will assume that the agent exhibits risk preference for small portfolios of low-risk (i.e. near the certainty line) but risk aversion everywhere else. On these assumptions he or she has indifference curves as indicated in Fig. 8.1.

Combining budget constraint and indifference curves presents a problem unusual in 'normal' consumer theory. For some values of R and L there are two utility maxima separated by a minimum. For others there is a single maximum. This is illustrated in Fig. 8.2 which shows expected utility as a function of L_a. As R and L change it is possible for one of the maxima of Fig. 8.2(i) to disappear, leaving a single maximum as in Fig. 8.2(ii). Making the assumption that the speculator is a *local*, rather than a *global* utility maximiser we evidently have here a case of 'disappearing equilibria' of the kind discussed in the introduction. As the local maximum at $L_a = X_1$ disappears there is a jump to $L_a = X_2$. Jumps in L_a correspond to jumps in D, since the two are related by equation (8.4).

Is it possible to characterise the relationship between R and L

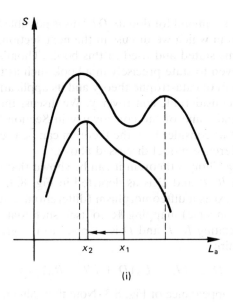

(i)

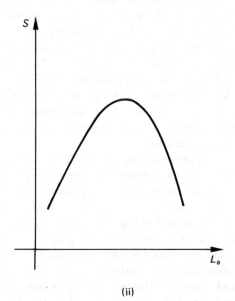

(ii)

Fig. 8.2

and the agent's demand for dollars D? This is possible by appeal to Thom's theorem which we discuss in the next section. Unlike the other theorems stated and used in this book, Thom's theorem is too difficult even to state precisely in a book such as this. It is the central theorem of catastrophe theory and its application has been the object of considerable controversy. We discuss the theorem in Section 8.3 and some of the controversy in Section 8.5. For the time being let us consider how the theorem can be used to analyse the state preference model discussed above.

By applying Thom's theorem it can be shown that the relationship between R, L and D is as depicted in Fig. 8.3. To be more precise there exists a diffeomorphism (differentiable function with differentiable inverse) mapping $\mathbb{R}^3$ to itself such that near point P the 'graph' relating R, L and D is mapped to the graph given by the relationship:

$$D^3 + (L - L_0)D + (R - R_0) = 0 \qquad (8.7)$$

which has the appearance of Fig. 8.3. Note that diffeomorphism is a kind of topological equivalence similar to the homeomorphisms discussed in Chapter 6. We may think of two geometrical objects as homeomorphic if one can be continuously deformed into the other without any breaking or joining. Diffeomorphism is slightly stricter, requiring in addition, no creasing or flattening of creases. Note also that Thom's theorem concerns a *local* diffeomorphism, near point P. We shall return to this point in Section 8.5 but in the meantime we make the (justifiable) assumption that the diffeomorphism holds good for a wide enough range of values of L and R to be useful in modelling.

Equation (8.7) represents the canonical (or 'standard') form of the *cusp catastrophe*. Anything diffeomorphic to this canonical form is also a cusp catastrophe. Certain standard features of catastrophe models can be illustrated by examining Fig. 8.3. The 'bifurcation set' illustrated in Fig. 8.3 is the projection of the folds in the graph into the R–L plane. It is depicted in Fig. 8.4. Consider an agent holding a constant and relatively small portfolio. Suppose now the exchange rate rises causing R to rise. We can trace out the agent's demand curve for dollars: it falls as the exchange rate r (£/$) rises and, as R reaches point A in the bifurcation set, experiences a sudden jump downwards. This is a catastrophic jump: it is illustrated in Fig. 8.5 which shows the agent's demand

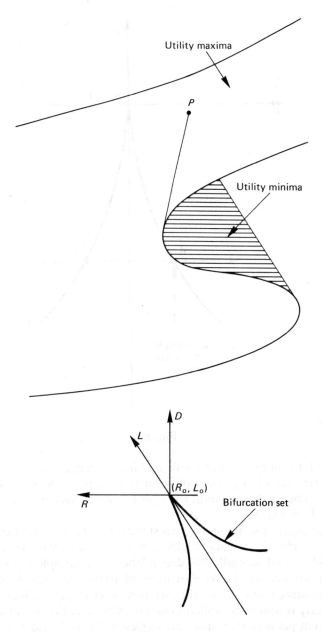

Fig. 8.3

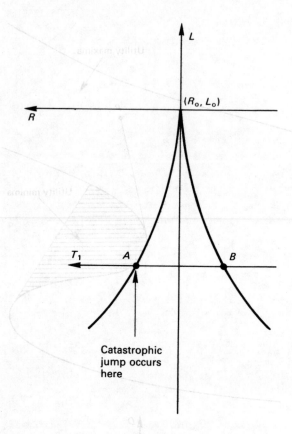

Fig. 8.4

curve for dollars. Consider now a falling exchange rate. It should be clear that a jump does not occur in demand at the same point ($r = r_1$) but is delayed until $r = r_2$ in Fig. 8.5. This corresponds to point B in Fig. 8.4.

The analysis so far shows two standard features of catastrophe models. Firstly the catastrophic jump, associated with vanishing equilibria and secondly the dependence of a variable (D in this case) not just on the *level* of the underlying variables R and L determining it but also on the *direction in which they change*. This property is sometimes called *hysteresis*. Consider Fig. 8.6 in which different paths in R, L space are depicted. Paths T_2 and T_3 lead to

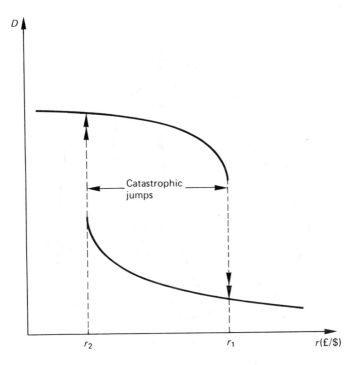

Fig. 8.5 A demand curve for dollars.

the same values of L and R but T_3 generates a higher demand for dollars. Paths T_4 and T_5 lead to the same value, of L, R and D but T_4 generates a jump in demand at point B, while T_5 entails smoothly changing demand.

The state-preference model with non-convexities has shown how catastrophe theory can be applied in economics. It might be argued, however, that non-convexities of preference become unimportant under aggregation (see for example, Rothenburg, 1960). This really depends on whether different agents' bifurcation sets are crossed simultaneously. In a market containing a large number of similar agents holding similar expectations this is quite possible. Such a situation is depicted in Fig. 8.7 where T_1 crosses several bifurcation sets in the small shaded area. Under these circumstances the market demand curve may well exhibit jumps.

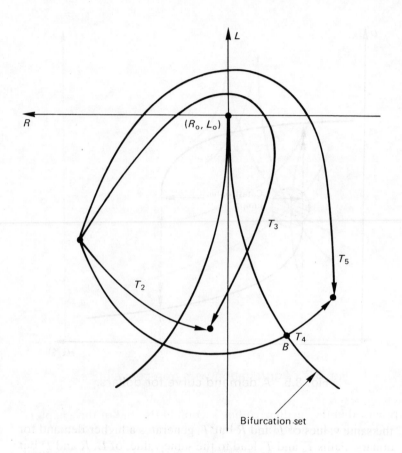

Fig. 8.6

8.3 Thom's theorem

The analysis of the previous section was based on the central theorem of catastrophe theory. It is a theorem which provides a kind of classification of discontinuities. Even to state the theorem precisely would take us beyond the scope of this book, but in this section a discussion of the theorem is provided which should help the reader understand its application. References on Thom's theorem and on the application of catastrophe theory in economics are

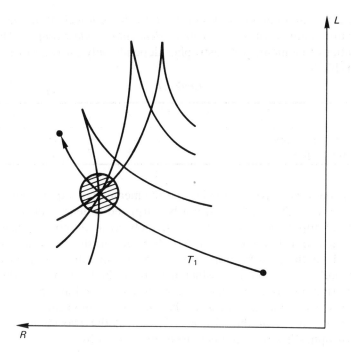

Fig. 8.7 Aggregation with non-convexities.

provided in the further reading section at the end of this chapter.
Consider a function f:

$$f : \mathbb{R}^{n+r} \to \mathbb{R} \qquad (8.8)$$

We think of f as having n variables denoted $\mathbf{x} \in \mathbb{R}^n$ and r parameters denoted $\mathbf{y} \in \mathbb{R}^r$ and suppose f to have all its partial derivatives, to any order (such a function is called *infinitely differentiable*). Now define the set:

$$M_f = \{ (\mathbf{x}, \mathbf{y}) \in \mathbb{R}^{n+r} : f_{x_i} = 0, \quad i = 1, \ldots, n \} \qquad (8.9)$$

M_f is simply the set (or graph) of turning points for the function f (with respect to the variables $x_1, \ldots, x_n$). We may think of f as a 'potential function' with the property that the behaviour of some system is governed by its maximisation or minimisation. Obvious examples in economics are utility and profit (maximisation) or cost (minimisation).

Discontinuities and catastrophes **145**

Thom's theorem tells us that for $r \leqslant 5$, M_f is equivalent to one of a finite number of types, called *elementary catastrophes*. The number of elementary catastrophes depends only on r, according to Table 8.1.

Table 8.1

r	1	2	3	4	5	$\geqslant 6$
No. of elementary catastrophes	1	2	5	7	11	∞

Of course we have not made clear the meaning of 'equivalent' in this context. The reader will not be surprised to learn that it is a form of topological equivalence, namely local diffeomorphism. The idea of a diffeomorphism was discussed in the previous section. Thus the classification provided by Thom's theorem is *local* and *qualitative*, two points which have been the focus of considerable criticism, some of which is considered in Section 8.5.

For each elementary catastrophe there is a canonical form for the function f. For the case $r = 2$, one of the two elementary catastrophes has the canonical form for f given by:

$$f(x; a, b) = x^4 + ax^2 + bx \qquad (8.10)$$

This is called the *cusp* catastrophe. Differentiating with respect to x gives the equation:

$$4x^3 + 2ax + b = 0 \qquad (8.11)$$

as defining the set M_f. The reader will readily be able to verify that a simple change of coordinates leads from equation (8.11) to equation (8.7) of the previous section. The eleven elementary catastrophes are set out in Table 8.2. Note that they come in two families, the *cuspoids*, which can be generated from potential functions of only one variable and the *umbilics* which require potential functions of at least two variables.

For all catastrophes the projection of the 'graph' M_f into parameter space is of particular importance. 'Folds' in M_f are projected into a subset of parameter space called the *bifurcation set*. Jumps in the variables $x_1 \ldots x_n$ can occur when parameters take values lying in this bifurcation set. This was illustrated in the previous section for the cusp catastrophe.

Table 8.2   The eleven elementary catastrophes

Catastrophe	Minimum n	Minimum r	Canonical potential function
Cuspoids			
Fold	1	1	$x^3 + ax$
Cusp	1	2	$x^4 + ax^2 + bx$
Swallowtail	1	3	$x^5 + ax^3 + bx^2 + cx$
Butterfly	1	4	$x^6 + ax^4 + bx^3 + cx^2 + dx$
Wigwam	1	5	$x^7 + ax^5 + bx^4 + cx^3 + dx^2 + fx$
Umbilics			
Elliptic umbilic	2	3	$x^3 - xy^2 + a(x^2 + y^2) + bx + cy$
Hyperbolic umbilic	2	3	$x^3 + y^3 + axy + bx + cy$
Parabolic umbilic	2	4	$y^4 + x^2y + ax^2 + by^2 + cx + dy$
Symbolic umbilic	2	5	$x^3 + y^4 + axy^2 + by^2 + cxy + dy + fx$
Second elliptic umbilic	2	5	$x^2y - y^5 + ay^3 + by^2 + cx^2 + dy + fy$
Second hyperbolic umbilic	2	5	$x^2y + y^5 + ay^3 + by^2 + cx^2 + dy + fx$

There seems to be a catch in Thom's theorem in that it refers to functions which are called 'generic'. Genericity is introduced to formalise the idea that f is a 'typical' function, and it turns out that any continuous function may be approximated arbitrarily closely by a generic function.

8.4 A trade cycle model

Kaldor (1940) has advanced a model of the trade cycle involving non-linear savings and investment functions. His model exhibits disappearing equilibria and sudden jumps of the kind discussed elsewhere in this chapter. In this section we show how Kaldor's model can be generalised using catastrophe theory.

Kaldor sets out a model of a closed, ungoverned economy in which planned investment (I) is a function of aggregate income (Y) and the capital stock (K):

$$I = I(Y, K) \tag{8.12}$$

and savings (S) depends on income

$$S = S(Y) \tag{8.13}$$

For various reasons he proposes a sigmoid form for investment and savings functions. As illustrated in Fig. 8.8 this leads to the possibility of multiple equilibria. The reader should be able readily to verify that the high and low-income equilibria (Y_1 and Y_3) are stable while the mid-income equilibrium (Y_2) is unstable.

Of course Y_1, Y_2 and Y_3 are only short-run equilibria. With income at a high level such as Y_1, net investment will be taking place and this is turn, will increase the capital stock, causing the investment function to shift downwards. Income falls gradually until eventually the two equilibria Y_1 and Y_2 merge and vanish leaving the single (low-income) equilibrium Y_3. (This is illustrated in Fig. 8.9.) The economy moves rapidly from Y_1 to Y_3: this is a catastrophic jump. Note that the equilibrium at Y_3 is stable. At this low level of income net capital accumulation is negative; the production of capital goods does not even make up for depreciation. As a consequence, the investment function shifts upwards again. Eventually the two equilibria Y_3 and Y_2 will coalesce and vanish, causing a jump to Y_1. This jump does not occur at the same

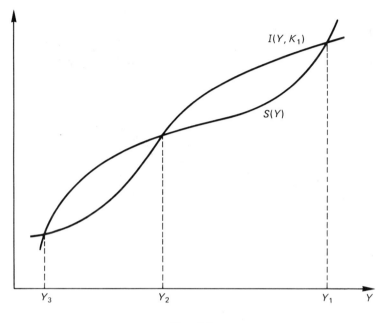

Fig. 8.8

income level as the demand jump in the previous phase of the trade cycle.

Fig. 8.10 shows the short-run equilibria of the economy and the arrows indicate its cyclical path. The double-headed arrows indicate rapid movements or jumps. The broken line segment indicates unstable equilibria such as Y_2.

We may formalise the model as a two-variable dynamical system of the kind discussed in Chapter 6. Suppose income (Y) adjusts at a rate proportional to excess demand. Then we have

$$\dot{Y} = A[C(Y) + I(Y, K) - Y] \qquad (8.14)$$

where C = consumption and A is a constant. We may readily write down an equation describing capital accumulation:

$$\dot{K} = I(Y, K) - I_R \qquad (8.15)$$

where I_R = replacement investment, assumed constant.

Equations (8.14) and (8.15) together constitute a two-dimensional non-linear dynamical system of which Fig. 8.11 is a phase portrait.

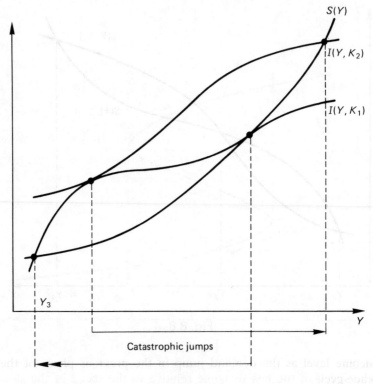

Fig. 8.9

This diagram is drawn on the assumption, implicit in Kaldor's mode, that the system has a unique unstable equilibrium (point E in Fig. 8.11). One could attempt to apply the linearisation technique of Chapter 6 to this dynamical system, but this approach proves fruitless. It is possible, however, to invoke the Poincaré–Bendixson theorem (this theorem is not discussed in this book, but the interested reader should consult Hirsch and Smale, 1974) in this case, to establish that this system has a limit cycle. (For another system with a limit cycle see equations (6.34).) Fast movement (jumps) are again indicated with double-headed arrows.

We may think of the dynamical system as consisting of a 'fast dynamic' causing rapid movement towards short-run equilibrium and a 'slow dynamic' causing slower changes in that equilibrium.

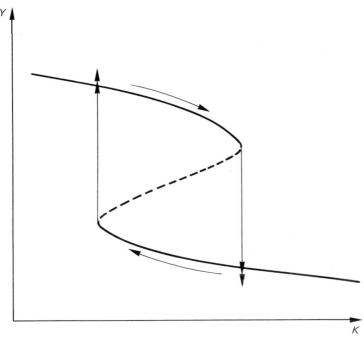

Fig. 8.10

The speed of the fast dynamic relative to the speed of the slow dynamic increases as one increases the constant, A, in equation (8.14). In other words, increasing A increases the 'suddenness' of the jumps in Y.

An obvious generalisation of Kaldor's model arises from noting that investment depends on the capital stock but that savings does not depend on consumer wealth. This asymmetry is easily removed by adopting a 'life-cycle' approach to savings and supposing therefore that an increase in consumer wealth (W) increases the marginal propensity to consume at all levels of income. This is indicated in Fig. 8.12 from which it is clear that at low levels of wealth there is only one equilibrium level of income and hence no possibility for catastrophic jumps. Equation (8.14) now becomes:

$$\dot{Y} = A[C(Y, W) + I(Y, K) - Y] \qquad (8.16)$$

By using Thom's theorem we can analyse the surface of short-run equilibria: that is the surface M, given by:

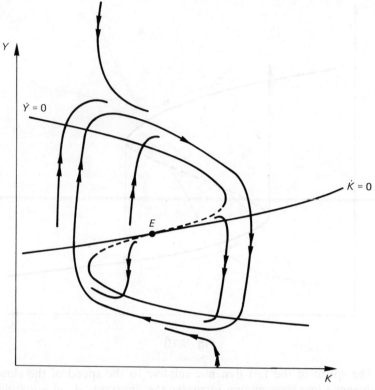

Fig. 8.11

$$M = \{(Y, W, K): \dot{Y} = 0\} \tag{8.17}$$

This turns out to be equivalent (in the sense of Section 8.3 above) to the cusp catastrophe surface and is depicted in Fig. 8.13.

A question arises as to how W can differ from K in an essentially one-good model. Private sector debt would simply 'wash-out' of the model on aggregation and, in the absence of a government, there can be no government debt. We interpret W as the present value of consumers' expected future incomes. Making it an expectational variable allows for some simple but interesting dynamics. Suppose that the adjustment of W is given by:

$$\dot{W} = F(Y, W, K) \tag{8.18}$$

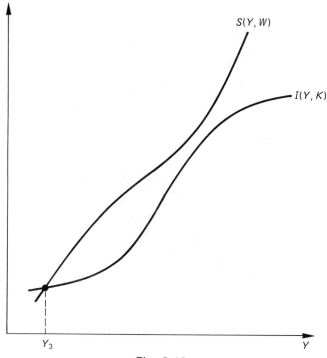

S(Y, W)

I(Y, K)

Y_3

Y

Fig. 8.12

and that the three-dimensional dynamical system given by (8.15), (8.16) and (8.18) has a single unstable equilibrium (Y^*, K^*, W^*). Suppose further that consumers' income expectations are related to current incomes. So that, when incomes are 'low' consumers revise their expectations downwards and when incomes are 'high' they revise them upwards. We may then adopt the following form for equation (8.18):

$$\dot{W} = m(Y - Y^*) \qquad (8.19)$$

where $m > 0$ is a constant.

The full dynamics of the dynamical system consisting of equations (8.16), (8.15) and (8.19) are depicted in Fig. 8.14. Note that income exhibits sudden falls and gradual recoveries while the stock variables change smoothly, without any jumps. The reader should readily be able to sketch time-paths for all variables of the model.

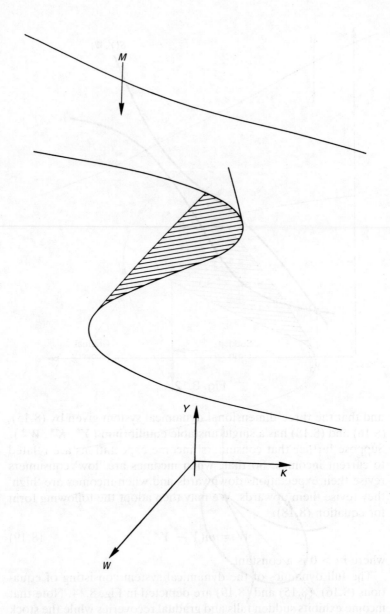

Fig. 8.13 Short-run equilibria of the trade–cycle model.

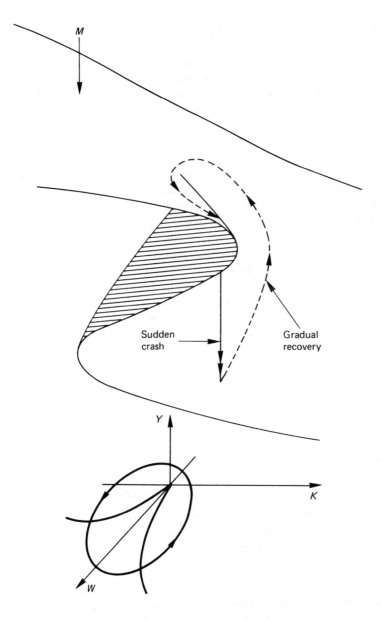

Fig. 8.14 Full dynamics of the trade–cycle model.

8.5 Methodological problems

Catastrophe theory has generated far more controversy than most branches of mathematics and much of this has surrounded its application. The best known critique is an article by Zahler and Sussman (1977) in *Nature*. In this section we consider some of the criticisms most relevant to economic applications.

Using catastrophe theory, models involving vanishing equilibria can be developed, since catastrophe theory tells us that equilibria can vanish and reappear in a limited number of ways. Each type of metamorphosis has a typical geometry and a canonical model. Such models can provide useful explanations of jump behaviour and hysteresis. Catastrophe theory only provides *qualitative* analysis however. It characterises relationships by means of topological equivalence (i.e. local diffeomorphism). The dangers of local as distinct from global analysis have been discussed in Chapter 6 in connection with Hartman's theorem (though here the form of equivalence was homeomorphism rather than diffeomorphism). The same dangers apply to the use of Thom's theorem, though it is often possible to avoid them by taking sufficient care in the analysis of particular models.

Perhaps more problematical is the qualitative nature of catastrophe theory. In the trade cycle model assumptions concerning the *general shape* (sigmoid) of investment and savings functions lead to conclusions concerning the *general shape* (cusp catastrophe) of the short-run relationship between Y K and W. This kind of reasoning is often appropriate in economics since it is rare that one has any basis for specifying exact functional forms. This is, however, of little help when one is faced with empirical questions of testing. Isnard and Zeeman (1975) remark that:

> if catastrophe theory is to be any use in the human sciences then its models must not only offer qualitative insight but must also be susceptible to quantitative testing.

Even a purely qualitative model can make a definite and precise statement about the world which data should be capable of accepting or rejecting. The standard econometric approach is unlikely to succeed, however, because of the qualitative nature of catastrophe models. There is no (known) measure of goodness of fit which is invariant to diffeomorphism. Note the contrast with the familiar linear econometric model where a finite number of parameters can express the general form of the model.

Catastrophe theory is mathematics of a 'qualitative' kind; but this need not be a disadvantage. It was developed originally with a view to applications in biology and in many respects economics is more similar to biology than it is to physics. It may well be that qualitative models turn out to be the most appropriate kind for economists to use.

Exercises

1 Consider an individual with a utility function in terms of two goods:

$$U(x, y) = x^4 + xy \qquad x,y > 0$$

He or she is subject to a budget constraint

$$px + y = m$$

  (i) Derive his or her utility function in terms of x, p and m, eliminating y.
 (ii) Sketch graphs of U against x for high values of p and for low values of p.
(iii) Derive an expression relating chosen values of x to given values of p and m and sketch a (3D) graph to illustrate this relationship.
 (iv) Assuming the individual to be a *local* utility maximiser, show that his or her demand behaviour may exhibit hysteresis and catastrophic jumps.

2 Derive the equation of the bifurcation set of the canonical cusp catastrophe.

Further reading

Woodcock and Davis (1978) is a popular introduction to catastrophe theory. Saunders (1980) is an excellent, slightly more advanced, reference which discusses both mathematics and applications. See also Poston and Stewart (1978). The classic reference, by the founder of catastrophe theory, is Thom (1976).

The economic applications in this chapter are taken from George (1981). See also Varian (1979), Harris (1976) and Fischer and Jammernegg (1986).

Zahler and Sussman (1977) is the most famous critique of applied catastrophe theory.

For a discussion of the problems of testing catastrophe models empirically see Cobb (1978, 1981).

Appendix
Brief solutions to
selected exercises

Chapter 2

1. [8, 17]
4. $Y_K = a\left[\dfrac{Q}{K}\right]^{1+\beta}$ $Y_L = b\left[\dfrac{Q}{L}\right]^{1+\beta}$
5. $(x, y) = (0, 0)$ and $(x, y) = \left(\dfrac{1}{6}, \dfrac{-1}{12}\right)$
7. (i) Yes   (ii) Yes, but it is not concave over the domain $[0, 2\pi]$ (iii) No, e.g. take α $\beta = 3/4$

Chapter 3

1 (a) Max $\pi = p_1 q_1 + p_2 q_2 - C(q_1, q_2) - K(y)$
   s.t. $q_1 \leqslant y$ (Multiplier λ_1)
        $q_2 \leqslant y$ (Multiplier λ_2)

   Lagrangian $L = p_1 q_1 + p_2 q_2 - C(q_1, q_2) - K(y) + \lambda_1[y - q_1] + \lambda_2[y - q_2]$

   (b) $L_{q_1} = p_1 - C_1 - \lambda_1 = 0$ (since $q_1 > 0$)   (1)
     $L_{q_2} = p_2 - C_2 - \lambda_2 = 0$ (since $q_2 > 0$)   (2)
     $L_y = -K'(y) + \lambda_1 + \lambda_2 = 0$ (since $y > 0$)   (3)

   Since $q_2 < y$ the Kuhn–Tucker theorem gives $\lambda_2 = 0$
   (i) Hence (2) $\Rightarrow \underline{p_2 = C_2}$

     and   (3) $\Rightarrow \lambda_1 = K'(y)$
   (ii) so   (1) $\Rightarrow \underline{p_1 = C_1 + K'(y)}$

2 (i) Max $PY - rR - wl$
     s.t. $Y \leqslant f(R_0, l)$ (Multiplier λ_1)
          $R \leqslant R_0$ (Multiplier λ_2)

Lagrangian $L = PY - rR - wl + \lambda_1 [f(R, l) - Y] + \lambda_2 (R_0 - R)$

$$\Rightarrow L_Y = P - \lambda_1 = 0 \qquad (Y > 0) \tag{1}$$
$$L_R = -r + \lambda_1 f_R - \lambda_2 = 0 \qquad (R > 0) \tag{2}$$
$$L_l = -w + \lambda_1 f_l = 0 \qquad (l > 0) \tag{3}$$

(1) and (3) $\Rightarrow$ $\underline{w = pf_l}$

(ii) Take $P > 0$ then (1) $\Rightarrow \lambda_1 > 0 \Rightarrow$ production function binding, by Theorem 3.3. If the resource constraint is binding, then:

$$\pi = Pf(R_0, l) - rR_0 - wl$$
$$\Rightarrow \quad \pi_{R_0} = Pf_{R_0} - r$$
$$= \lambda_2 \qquad \text{(by (2) and (1))}$$

If the constraint is not binding then $\pi_{R_0} = 0$; and $\lambda_2 = 0$ (by theorem 3.3).

Chapter 4

2 (i) *Primal*

Min. $x_1 + x_2 + x_3$

s.t. $\dfrac{1}{40} x_1 + \dfrac{1}{50} x_2 + \dfrac{1}{70} x_3 \geq 10$ (dual variable a)

     $\dfrac{1}{60} x_1 + \dfrac{1}{25} x_2 + \dfrac{1}{20} x_3 \geq 4$ (dual variable b)

     $x_1, x_2, x_3 \geq 0$

Dual

Max $10a + 4b$

s.t. $\dfrac{1}{40} a + \dfrac{1}{60} b \leq 1$ (primal variable x_1)

     $\dfrac{1}{50} a + \dfrac{1}{25} b \leq 1$ (primal variable x_2)

     $\dfrac{1}{70} a + \dfrac{1}{20} b \leq 1$ (primal variable x_3)

(ii) $a = 40$, $b = 0$: only x_1 constraint binds $\Rightarrow x_2 = x_3 = 0$, by duality. Also $a > 0$ hence a-constraint binds, by duality. This gives $x_1 = 400$, $x_2 = 0$, $x_3 = 0$.

(iii) Dual solution is now such that a, $b > 0$ x_1 and x_2 constraints binding but x_3 constraint slack. Using duality theorems as in (i) yields $x_1 = 480$, $x_2 = 100$, $x_3 = 0$

Chapter 5

1

$$\begin{vmatrix} \frac{1}{2} - \lambda & \frac{1}{2} \\ \frac{1}{8} & \frac{1}{2} - \lambda \end{vmatrix} = \left[\frac{1}{2} - \lambda \right]\left[\frac{1}{2} - \lambda \right] - \frac{1}{16} = 0$$

$$\Rightarrow \lambda^2 - \lambda + \frac{3}{16} = 0$$

$$\Rightarrow \lambda = \frac{1}{4}, \frac{3}{4} < 1$$

Hence, by Perron–Frobenius theorem, the matrix is productive.

$$q = (I - A)^{-1}\begin{bmatrix} 2 \\ 1 \end{bmatrix} = \begin{bmatrix} \frac{1}{2} & -\frac{1}{2} \\ -\frac{1}{8} & \frac{1}{2} \end{bmatrix}^{-1}\begin{bmatrix} 2 \\ 1 \end{bmatrix} = \frac{16}{3}\begin{bmatrix} \frac{1}{2} & -\frac{1}{2} \\ \frac{1}{8} & \frac{1}{2} \end{bmatrix}\begin{bmatrix} 2 \\ 1 \end{bmatrix} = \begin{bmatrix} 8 \\ 4 \end{bmatrix}$$

5 (i) $x_1 + 3x_2 \geqslant 3$
$\qquad x_1 + 2x_2 \geqslant 5$

(ii) Min. $x_1 + x_2$
$\quad$ s.t. $\quad x_1 + 3x_2 \geqslant 3$
$\qquad\qquad x_1 + 2x_2 \geqslant 5$
$\qquad\qquad x_1, x_2 \geqslant 0$

Solution: $x_1 = 0$, $x_2 = \frac{5}{2}$

$\Rightarrow$ value of wage bundle $= 0 + \frac{5}{2} = \frac{5}{2}$

(iii) It is not.

6 $P_1 b_1 = (1 + r) a_1 P_1 + w$ $\qquad\qquad\qquad\qquad\qquad$ (1)
$\quad\; b_2 = (1 + r) a_2 P_1 + w$ $\qquad\qquad\qquad\qquad\qquad$ (2)
$\; P_3 b_3 = (1 + r) a_3 P_1 + w$ $\qquad\qquad\qquad\qquad\qquad$ (3)

(2) $\Rightarrow P_1 = \dfrac{b_2 - w}{(1+r)\, a_2}$

Substitute in (1):

$$\frac{(b_2 - w)b_1}{(1 + r)\, a_2} = \frac{a_1(b_2 - w)}{a_2} + w$$

$$\Rightarrow (b_2 - w)b_1 = a_1(b_2-w)(1 + r) + w(1 + r)a_2$$
$$= (1 + r)[a_1 b_2 + w(a_2 - a_1)]$$

$$\Rightarrow 1 + r = \frac{b_1(b_2 - w)}{a_1 b_2 + (a_2 - a_1)w} \qquad\qquad\qquad (4)$$

(ii) Exogenous w together with (4) determine r *independently* of a_3 and b_3. Hence (1) or (2) determine P_1 independently of a_3 and b_3. Hence, from (3), variations in a_3 and b_3 will affect P_3.

Chapter 6

1 $\dfrac{dy}{dx} = \dfrac{y+1}{x-1} \Rightarrow \dfrac{1}{y+1}\dfrac{dy}{dx} = \dfrac{1}{x-1}$

    $\Rightarrow \log(y+1) = \log(x-1) + \text{constant}$ (integrating)
    $\Rightarrow y + 1 = A(x-1)$ $(A = \text{constant})$
    $\Rightarrow$ Hence $A = -3$ from boundary condition
    Hence $\underline{y = 2-3x}$

4   (a) $\dfrac{\dot{y}}{y} = a + \alpha\left[\dfrac{\dot{k}}{k}\right]$

    $\Rightarrow \log y = at + \log k + \text{constant}$ (integrating)
    $\Rightarrow y = Ae^{at}k^{\alpha}$ $(A = \text{constant})$
    $\Rightarrow \dfrac{Y}{L} = Ae^{at}\left[\dfrac{K}{L}\right]^{\alpha}$

    $\underline{\Rightarrow Y = Ae^{at}K^{\alpha}L^{1-\alpha}}$

    (b) $\dot{K} = S = sP$ (from (i) and (iii))
       $\Rightarrow \dfrac{\dot{K}}{K} = \dfrac{sP}{K} = \dfrac{s}{\beta}\left[\dfrac{K}{Y} - \gamma\right]$ (from (ii))

       $\Rightarrow \dfrac{\dot{K}}{K} - \dfrac{s}{\beta}\dfrac{K}{Y} + \dfrac{s\gamma}{\beta} = 0$

5   (i) $\dot{K}_1 = \theta I = \theta\beta K_1$
      $\Rightarrow K_1 = K_1(0)e^{\theta\beta t}$ (integrating)
      $\underline{\Rightarrow I = \beta K_1(0)e^{\theta\beta t}}$ (1)

      $\dot{K}_2 = (1-\theta)I = (1-\theta)\beta K_1$
      $\Rightarrow \dot{K}_2 = (1-\theta)\beta K_1(0)e^{\theta\beta t}$ (2)

    Integrating gives:

    $K_2 = \dfrac{(1-\theta)\beta K_1(0) e^{\theta\beta t}}{\theta\beta} + \gamma$ $(\gamma = \text{constant})$

    $K_2 = \dfrac{(1-\theta) K_1(0) e^{\theta\beta t}}{\theta} + \gamma$

    Taking $t = 0$:

    $K_2(0) = \dfrac{(1-\theta)}{\theta} K_1(0) + \gamma$

    $\Rightarrow \gamma = K_2(0) + \dfrac{(\theta-1)}{\theta} K_1(0)$

    Hence $C = K_2 = \dfrac{(1-\theta)}{\theta} K_1(0)e^{\theta\beta t} + K_2(0) + \dfrac{(\theta-1)}{\theta} K_1(0)$

    $\underline{\Rightarrow C = (e^{\theta\beta t} - 1)\dfrac{(1-\theta)}{\theta} K_1(0) + K_2(0)}$

$$\frac{\dot{C}}{C} = \frac{(1-\theta)\beta K_1(0) e^{\theta\beta t}}{\frac{(1-\theta) K_1(0) e^{\theta\beta t} + \gamma}{\theta}} \qquad \text{(from (2) and (3))}$$

$$\text{Hence: } \frac{\dot{C}}{C} = \frac{\theta\beta}{1 + \frac{\gamma\theta e^{-\theta\beta t}}{(1-\theta) K_1(0)}}$$

$$\frac{\dot{C}}{C} \to \theta\beta \text{ as } t \to \infty$$

and from (1) $\dfrac{\dot{I}}{I} = \theta\beta$

Chapter 7

1 (i) Max $\int_0^\infty (pF - F^2) e^{-rt} dt$
   s.t. $\dot{Q} = A \log BQ - F$ (costate variable λ)
   Q_0 given

   Hamiltonian is:

   $H = (pF - F^2) e^{-rt} + \lambda (A \log BQ - F)$
   Pontryagin necessary conditions:

   $$-\dot{\lambda} = H_Q = \frac{\lambda A}{Q} \qquad (1)$$
   $$0 = H_F = (p - 2F)e^{-rt} - \lambda \qquad (2)$$

   (ii) (2) $\Rightarrow \lambda e^{rt} = p - 2F$ $\qquad (3)$
   $\Rightarrow \dot{\lambda} e^{rt} + r e^{rt}\lambda = -2\dot{F}$

   (differentiating w.r.t. time)

   $\Rightarrow \qquad (r\lambda + \dot{\lambda})e^{rt} = -2\dot{F}$

   $\Rightarrow \qquad (r - \dfrac{\lambda A}{Q}) e^{rt} = -2\dot{F} \qquad \text{(from (1))}$

   $\Rightarrow \qquad (r - \dfrac{A}{Q}) \lambda e^{rt} = -2\dot{F}$

   $\Rightarrow \qquad (r - \dfrac{A}{Q}) (p - 2F) = -2\dot{F} \qquad \text{(from (3))}$

   $\Rightarrow \qquad \dot{F} = -\frac{1}{2} (r - \dfrac{A}{Q}) (p - 2F)$

2 (i) Max $\int_0^\infty [pq - q^3 - k] e^{-rt} dt$
   s.t. $\dot{x} = \alpha x - \beta y^2 - q$ (costate variable λ_1)
   $\dot{y} = -k$ (costate variable λ_2)

Hamiltonian is:

$$H = [pq - q^3 - k]e^{-rt} + \lambda_1[\alpha x - \beta y^2 - q]$$
$$- \lambda_2 k$$

Pontryagin necessary conditions:

$$H_x = \lambda_1 \alpha = -\dot{\lambda}_1 \qquad\qquad (1)$$
$$H_y = -\lambda_1 2\beta y = -\dot{\lambda}_2 \qquad (2)$$
$$H_q = [p - 3q^2]e^{-rt} - \lambda_1 = 0 \qquad (3)$$
$$H_k = -e^{-rt} - \lambda_2 = 0 \qquad (4)$$

(ii) $\lambda_1 = \lambda_1(0)e^{-\alpha t}$ (from (1))   (5)

$\lambda_2 = -e^{-rt}$ (from (4))

$\Rightarrow \dot{\lambda}_2 = re^{-rt}$

$\Rightarrow re^{-rt} = \lambda_1 2\beta y$ (from (2))

$$\Rightarrow y = \frac{re^{(\alpha - r)t}}{2\lambda_1(0)\beta} \qquad \text{(from (5))}$$

But $\lambda_1(0) = [p - 3q^2(0)]\,e^{-rt}$ (from (3))

Hence, $y = \dfrac{re^{\alpha t}}{2\beta[p - 3q^2(0)]}$

Bibliography

ARROWSMITH, D.K. and C.M. PLACE (1982) *Ordinary Differential Equations* (Chapman & Hall).

BAUMOL, W.J. (1977) *Economic Theory and Operations Analysis*, 4th edn (Prentice-Hall).

BAUMOL, W.J. (1967) *Business Behavior, Value and Growth* (Harcourt Brace Jovanovich Inc.).

BAUMOL, W.J. (1958) 'Topology of Second-Order Linear Difference Equations with Constant Coefficients', *Econometrica*, vol. 26.

BEGG, D.H.K. (1982) *The Rational Expectations Revolution in Macroeconomics* (Philip Allan).

BLAUG, M. (1980) *The Methodology of Economics or how economists explain* (CUP).

BROOME, J. (1983) *The Microeconomics of Capitalism* (Academic Press).

BUITER, W. and M. MILLER (1981) 'Monetary Policy and International Competitiveness; the Problem of Adjustment', in W. Eltis and P. Sinclair (eds). *The Money Supply and the Exchange Rate* (OUP).

CARTER, M. and R. MADDOCK (1984) *Rational Expectations: Macroeconomics for the 1980s?* (Macmillan).

CHIANG, A.C. (1984) *Fundamental Methods of Mathematical Economics 3rd edn* (McGraw-Hill).

CHOW, G.C. (1973) 'Problems of Economic Policy from the Viewpoint of Optimal Control', *American Economic Review*.

COBB, L. (1978) 'Stochastic Catastrophe Models and Multimodal Distributions', *Behavioural Science*, vol. 23.

COBB, L. (1981) 'Parameter Estimation for the Cusp Catastrophe Model', *Behavioural Science*, vol. 26.

COVICK, O.E. (1974) 'The Quantity Theory of Drink — A Restatement', *Australian Economic Papers*.

CYERT, R.M. and J.G. MARCH (1963) *A Behavioral Theory of the Firm* (Prentice-Hall Inc.).

DANTZIG, G.B. (1951) 'Maximisation of a Linear Function of Variables Subject to Linear Inequalities', in T.C. Koopmans (ed.) *Activity Analysis of Production and Allocation* (Wiley).

DEBREU, G. (1959) *Theory of Value* (Cowles Foundation).

DESAI, M. (1973) 'Growth Cycles and Inflation in a Model of the Class Struggle', *Journal of Economic Theory*, vol. 6.

DIXIT, A.K. (1976) *Optimisation in Economic Theory* (Oxford University Press).

DORFMAN, R., P.A. SAMUELSON and R.M. SOLOW (1958) *Linear Programming and Economic Analysis* (McGraw-Hill).

DORFMAN, R. (1969) 'An Economic Interpretation of Optimal Control Theory', *American Economic Review*.

EDGEWORTH, F.Y. (1881) *Mathematical Psychics* (C. Kegan Paul & Co.).

FISCHER, E.O. and W. JAMMERNEGG (1986) 'Empirical Investigation of a Catastrophe Theory Extension of the Phillips Curve', *Review of Economics and Statistics*.

FRIEDMAN, M. and L.J. SAVAGE (1948) 'The Utility Analysis of Choices Involving Risk', *Journal of Political Economy*, vol. 56.

GALE, D. (1960) *The Theory of Linear Economic Models* (McGraw-Hill).

GEORGE, D.A.R. and L.T. OXLEY (1985) 'Structural Stability and Model Design', *Economic Modelling*.

GEORGE, D.A.R. (1981) 'Equilibrium and Catastrophes in Economics', *Scottish Journal of Political Economy*, vol. 28.

GEORGE, D.A.R. (1982) 'Worker Participation and Self-Management', *Scottish Journal of Political Economy*.

GOODWIN, R.M. (1951) 'The Non-linear Accelerator and the Persistence of Business Cycles', *Econometrica*, vol. 19.

GREEN, H.A.J. (1976) *Consumer Theory. Revised edn* (Macmillan).

HARCOURT, G.C. (1972), *Some Cambridge Controversies in the Theory of Capital* (CUP).

HARRIS, L. (1976) 'Catastrophe Theory, Utility Theory and Animal Spirits Expectations', *Australian Economic Papers*.

HICKS, J.R. (1950) *A Contribution to the Theory of The Trade Cycle* (OUP).

HIRSCH, M.W. and S. SMALE (1974) *Differential Equations, Dynamical Systems and Linear Algebra* (Academic Press).

INTRILLIGATOR, M.D. (1971) *Mathematical Optimisation and Economic Theory* (Prentice-Hall).

IRELAND, N.J. and P.J. LAW (1982) *The Economics of Labour-Managed Enterprises* (Croom Helm).

ISNARD, C.A. and E.C. ZEEMAN (1975) 'Some Models from Catastrophe Theory in the Social Sciences', in L. Collins (ed.) *The Use of Models in the Social Sciences* (Tavistock).

JEVONS, W.S. (1965) *The Theory of Political Economy*, 5th edn (Augustus M. Kelley).

JONES D.C. and J. SVEJNAR (eds) (1982) *Participatory and Self-Managed Firms* (Heath).

KALDOR, N. (1940) 'A Model at the Trade Cycle', *Economic Journal*, vol. 50.

KANTOROVICH, L.V. (1959) *The Best Use of Economic Resources*, extract reprinted in PME Readings in *Socialist Economics* (A. Nove and D.M. Nuti, (eds) (Penguin, 1972).

KATOUZIAN, H. (1980) *Ideology and Method in Economics* (Macmillan).

KOOPMANS, T.C. (1957) *Three Essays on the State of Economic Science* (McGraw-Hill).

KUHN, H.W. and A.W. TUCKER (1951) 'Nonlinear Programming' in J. Neyman (ed.) *Proceedings of the Second Berkeley Symposium on Mathematical Statistics and Probability* (University of California Press).

KUHN, T.S. (1970) *The Structure of Scientific Revolutions*, 2nd edn (Chicago).

LEIJONHUFVUD, A. (1981) 'Life among the Econ', in A. Leijonhufvud: *Information and Coordination* (OUP, 1981).

MAINWARING, L. (1984) *Value and Distribution in Capitalist Economies* (OUP).

MORISHIMA, M. (1973) *Marx's Economics: A Dual Theory of Value and Growth* (CUP).

NELSON, R.R. and S.G. WINTER (1982) *An Evolutionary Theory of Economic Change* (Harvard University Press).

NOVE, A. and D.M. NUTI (eds) (1972) *Socialist Economics* (Penguin).

PASINETTI, L.L. (1977) *Lectures on the Theory of Production* (Macmillan).

PETERSEN, F.M. and A.C. FISHER (1977) 'The Exploitation of Extractive Resources: A Survey', *Economic Journal*.

PHELPS, E. (1981) 'The Golden Rule of Accumulation: a Fable for Growthmen', *American Economic Review*.

PONTRYAGIN, L.S. *et al.* (1962) *A Mathematical Theory of Optimal Processes* (Wiley/Interscience).

POPPER, K.R. (1959) *The Logic of Scientific Discovery* (Hutchinson).

POSTON, T. and I. STEWART (1978), *Catastrophe Theory and its Applications* (Pitman).

RAMSEY, F.P. (1928) 'A Mathematical Theory of Saving', *Economic Journal*, vol. 38.

ROBINSON, J. (1934) 'Euler's Theorem and the Problem of Distribution', *Economic Journal*.

ROTHENBURG, T. (1960) 'Non-convexity, Aggregation and Pareto Optimality', *Journal of Political Economy*, vol. 68.

SAUNDERS, P.T. (1980) *An Introduction to Catastrophe Theory* (CUP).

SIMON, H.A. (1959) 'Theories of Decision Making in Economics', *American Economic Review*, vol. XLIX.

SIMON, H.A. (1957) *Models of Man* (John Wiley & Sons. Inc.).

STEEDMAN, I. (1977) *Marx after Sraffa* (New Left Books).

STEPHEN, F.H. (ed.) (1982) *The Performance of Labour-Managed Firms* (Macmillan).

STEWART, I.M.T. (1979) *Reasoning and Method in Economics* (McGraw-Hill).

THOM, R. (1976) *Structural Stability and Morphogenesis* (English Translation) (Benjamin).

VANEK, J.K. (1970) *The General Theory of Labour-Managed Market Economies* (Cornell, UP).
VARIAN, H.R. (1979) 'Catastrophe Theory and the Business Cycle', *Economic Inquiry*, vol. 27.
WICKSTEED, P.H. (1894) *Co-ordination of the Laws of Distribution*.
WOODCOCK, A. and M. DAVIS (1978) *Catastrophe Theory* (Penguin).
ZAHLER, R.S. and H.J. SUSSMAN (1977) 'Claims and Accomplishments of Applied Catastrophe Theory', *Nature*.

Index